D1097647

Renaissance
and Baroque
Drawings

RENAISSANCE AND BAROQUE DRAWINGS

FROM THE COLLECTIONS OF
JOHN AND ALICE STEINER

Edited by Konrad Oberhuber

FOGG ART MUSEUM

CAMBRIDGE · MASSACHUSETTS

1977

THIS CATALOGUE was prepared to accompany the exhibition *Renaissance and Baroque Drawings from the Collections of John and Alice Steiner*, Fogg Art Museum, Harvard University, November 18, 1977 – January 15, 1978, the Sterling and Francine Clark Art Institute, Williamstown, Massachusetts, February 7 – March 20, 1978, and the J. Paul Getty Museum, April 17 – June 17, 1978

ITALIAN DRAWINGS in this catalogue are from the collection of John Steiner. Northern Drawings are from the collection of Alice Steiner.

ON THE COVER: Perino del Vaga, *Studies of Horses*, cat. no. 34.
ON THE TITLE PAGE: Giovanni Battista Franco, *Design for the Decoration of an Apse*, cat. no. 13 (detail).

LIBRARY OF CONGRESS Cataloging in Publication Data
Main entry under title:
Renaissance and Baroque drawings from the collections of John and Alice Steiner.
Bibliography: p. 156
1. Drawing, Renaissance—Catalogs. 2. Drawing, Baroque—Catalogs. 3. Steiner, John H., 1903– —Art collections. 4. Steiner, Alice F., 1912– —Art collections. I. Harvard University. William Hayes Fogg Art Museum.
NC85.R46   741.9'4'07401444   77–11047
ISBN 0–916724–07–7

THE CATALOGUE was designed by Stephen Harvard, composed by The Stinehour Press, and printed by The Meriden Gravure Company.

Contents

Preface

R ENAISSANCE AND BAROQUE DRAWINGS
FROM THE COLLECTIONS OF JOHN AND
ALICE STEINER affords a welcome opportunity to acknowledge the enormous debt that a teaching museum owes the private
collector. The incomparable experience of collecting works of art,
a happy fact of professional life for the curator, is hard to come by
in a student's career, no matter how broad based and practical the
training program. Patient and generous collectors like the Steiners
fill the gap for our fortunate students. In opening their home and
making their extraordinary collection of master drawings available
to Konrad Oberhuber and his students, these kind people have added
a precious dimension to their education that their teachers can never
provide in classrooms or galleries.

The Museum is proud to share some of the Steiners' masterworks
with visitors in Cambridge and subsequently in Williamstown,
where the show will be exhibited at the Sterling and Francine Clark
Art Institute. This exhibition and catalogue continue the longstand-
ing Fogg tradition of bringing before the public distinguished private collections of drawings, among them those of Curtis Baer,
David Daniels, Louise and Joseph Pulitzer, Jr., and Freddy and
Regina Homburger, to name a few. With Professor Oberhuber's
help we shall continue to add other significant drawing collections to
this company in future years.

SEYMOUR SLIVE
Director, Fogg Art Museum

7

Foreword

AT THE SUGGESTION OF THE EDITOR of this catalogue, our friend Konrad Oberhuber, we are glad to say a few words about our collecting activity.

With a lifelong general interest in art, it was natural for us to start collecting when circumstances permitted. We bought our first drawing only in May 1971. This took place at Parke Bernet. Peter Wilson's gavel came down and made us the proud owners of a lovely *trois crayons* girl's head attributed to Rubens. We had no idea where this first step would lead us, how much research, correspondence, even travel would result from just that one purchase. After this first acquisition we wanted to know a good deal more about drawings. We therefore spent many hours a day for weeks on end at the Drawing Department of the Metropolitan Museum, where we got a friendly and helpful reception from Jacob Bean and his staff. We worked our way through the alphabet, from what seemed like hundreds of drawings by Allegrini through to the Zuccaros, and then did the same with Dutch and Flemish drawings. We looked and looked, we listened to friendly pointers and advice, and finally we even began to see things in the drawings ourselves.

We branched out in all directions: we read books, sat in on lectures, visited dealers, studied auction catalogues, subscribed to *Master Drawings*, and entered into lively correspondence with art historians here and abroad whenever a likeable drawing of unsure attribution presented itself to us, sometimes only after we had already bought it. Many experts were extremely cooperative and friendly. Gradually the collection grew. Of course we made mistakes, too. This did not deter us from new searches, however, even though such disappointments did discourage us for a little while.

At first we did not concentrate our efforts on any particular period. Later, reason told us that we would get lost in too wide a field and we started to limit ourselves to the sixteenth and seventeenth centuries, with occasional excursions into the eighteenth.

There were highs and lows in our activities. The lows we have described, and they were mostly soon forgotten, although they rankled a little. We are grateful that the highs were more numerous: at first almost any purchase delighted us, and then, as we became more discriminating, a deep satisfaction could be obtained only by acquiring something extraordinary, such as the Perino *Horses* or the Guercino *Seated Man* in red chalk. Once we became completely obsessed with the Castiglione *Crucifixion* (seen briefly in London by one of us on the way to an Amsterdam sale) only to find that by the time we got the photograph the drawing had been reserved for a museum whose curator would not make up her mind. It took considerable time and effort to get the staid old Bond Street firm which had the drawing to request the necessary answer, so that after months of waiting, correspondence, overseas cables, and telephone calls, in the end we got it.

Another highlight was the purchase of the Parmigianino and Bronzino drawings, which were so clear in the photographs (and had been seen by one of our expert friends beforehand) that we dared to buy them by overseas telephone from our home at 6 a.m., participating in the sale from lot number 1 and waiting with bated breath for the good word from the auctioneer.

And what a delight it was, after a disappointing morning at an Amsterdam sale, to get the two Dutch beauties—Doomer and Roghman—in the afternoon.

Obviously a bright event was a call from Konrad Oberhuber, informing us that he had discovered a Titian drawing in London. This serenely beautiful drawing also found its way into our collection and was included in the exhibition "I Disegni di Tiziano e della sua Cerchia" at the Fondazione Cini in Venice.

And how can one describe the elation of acquiring a Rembrandt by telephone participation in an auction sale at Amsterdam, which incidentally was done from a hospital bed in New York after some surgery!

As it became known that we were collecting Old Master drawings, some museum people and fellow collectors started to take an interest in our doings and came to see us. We got frank comments, some very complimentary, others somewhat critical, but we always enjoyed our visitors' company and valued their opinions. Eventually some of our drawings fitted into museum exhibitions with special topics.

When Dr. Oberhuber suggested last year that he would like to come to our house with a group of students, so that they could select a certain number of our drawings to study and catalogue preparatory to an exhibition at the Fogg, it was a great pleasure for us to watch the students' eager and earnest interest. We only hope that they found the visit as rewarding as we did and that all or some of them may become great art historians or museum people.

Over these years, we had joys and disappointments. Throughout it all, the drawings are with us, to look at and to live with and to enjoy. We try to understand what the artist meant and do research where indicated.

In these troubled times we are happy to have this oasis, which absorbs our interest and energy, gives us satisfaction and joy, and adds meaning to our lives.

We would like to use the opportunity of this exhibition and catalogue, this landmark in our collecting activity, to say that we could never have put together a worthwhile collection without the generous help and advice from so many wonderful people in this field. To all of them go our thanks, our gratitude, and our good wishes.

JOHN AND ALICE STEINER

List of Illustrations

NORTHERN DRAWINGS

Introduction

Renaissance and Baroque Drawings

IT IS ASTONISHING HOW MANY ASPECTS of Renaissance and Baroque draughtsmanship can be elucidated with examples from the collections of John and Alice Steiner, even with only the sheets chosen for this exhibition. The earliest Italian drawings in this catalogue are three works of the High Renaissance: the *Drapery Study* by Fra Bartolommeo shows the impressive grandeur and monumentality achieved in Florence around 1510; a *Sketchbook Sheet of Ornamental Studies* created in Rome only shortly later, probably by Giovanni da Udine, Raphael's great decorator, is an example of the perfect assimilation of the antique style achieved under this master's guidance between 1510 and 1520. Finally, Titian's extraordinary *Trees near Some Water*, a serene and rich evocation of nature unfolding in light and color, is a most splendid expression of the greatest contribution of Venice to sixteenth-century art.

The *Virgin and Child with Saints* by Domenico Campagnola, Titian's pupil, teaches us how the next generation moves on to a more highly expressive style, sacrificing both the naturalism and the serene grandeur of their mentors. His drawing shares with Perino del Vaga's mighty *Saint Peter* and magnificent *Studies of Horses*, as well as with Giulio Romano's sensuous *Putto on a Crouching Horse*, the rhythmic line moving through both composition and figures, creating an expressive language of its own. In the earlier drawings line was totally subordinated to the form it evoked. The later artists take delight in the forms on the plane of the sheet and the patterns the pen creates, an enjoyment that is as important to them as the subjects they depict. Prime expression of this joy in line and in formal beauty for its own sake is Parmigianino's *Minerva*, paradigm of the elegance

14

some artists sought in the third and fourth decades of the century.

The art of the next generation, that of Vasari, Bronzino, and Cambiaso, moves toward heavier forms and more somber expression. The linear rhythms no longer float freely from shape to shape but are caught in strongly outlined and volumetrically defined forms, which they force into contorted, ornamental shapes. In Bronzino's *Study of a Male Nude* this tendency toward the isolation of straining and expressive bodies into forms of an almost hieroglyphic quality reaches a culmination point. There is hardly a drawing that could better represent this style. The strongly abstracting tendency accompanying this phase of sixteenth-century art appears beautifully illustrated in Cambiaso's *Annunciation* with its clear, sharp contrasts of light and expressive foreshortening of the figures in space. These were major contributions of Genoa to Upper Italian art.

Taddeo Zuccaro, the dominant master of Rome in the fifties and sixties, prepares the later phase of Italian sixteenth-century art with his more dynamically interlocking forms. The artists of the end of the century are represented by the Roman Cavaliere d'Arpino, Malosso from the Upper Italian city of Cremona, the Milanese Giovanni Battista della Rovere, and Palma Giovane of Venice. They all utilize a crisp linear, often diagonal structure in their compositions and a strong sense for abstraction of the individual forms into weightless geometric shapes fitting into this intellectually clear network of relationships. A silvery light predominates. The Veronese Girolamo dai Paesi proves that even landscape can be evoked with such abstract schemes and hard-edged contrasts of light and shape.

The Carracci led the revolt against this style at the end of the sixteenth and the beginning of the seventeenth century. Lodovico's grand and elegant figures swing and bend, swayed by the emotions that pass through them; the sensuous presence of Annibale's *Venus* is achieved with a new painterly richness and sense of classical form. An engaging individual addresses us from Ottavio Leoni's *Portrait*, his inner feelings apparent in the face, especially in the large eyes and slightly open mouth.

A new landscape arises. In Gobbo's work the valleys and mountains surrounding the imposing castle assume a solid, clear structure and bodily presence articulated with the simplest of linear patterns; in Tassi's drawing the poetic light pervading the trees and hills takes human shape in the goddess Diana. Cantagallina leads us into the peaceful environs of a Tuscan villa lovingly observed in its quiet atmosphere. It is this same everyday world that Stefano della Bella, Tassi's compatriot, evokes with such caressing delicacy of stroke.

The next generation of artists wanted to express emotions with greater pathos: Guercino's *Seated Male Figure* throws back his head in a passionate gesture and reaches out eloquently to the side; Canuti's *Prophet* delivers his message with deep involvement and a glance full of profound feeling. The light pervades the draperies and bodies in Mola's *Immaculate Conception* and dissolves the material in order to evoke the movements of the soul with greater force. In Castiglione's *Crucifixion* the Virgin swoons before the Cross over which God the Father hovers with arms spread wide. We are drawn into a grand religious spectacle, a *theatrum sacrum*, like that constructed by Volterrano for the canonization of Santa Maria Maddalena dei Pazzi in Florence.

Even the profane life is pervaded by this fervent spirit, as in Rosa's *Studies* for a heroic battle or Guercino's *Portrait*, where the subject presents himself inflated with a new sense of his social importance. When Poussin, the great French classical artist, copies reliefs from *Trajan's Column* we can feel his deep emotional involvement even through his formal constraint. Emotion is also released in laughter. Caricature, a Baroque invention first practiced by the Carracci, is hilarious when Mola tries his hand at it.

Again the emotional intensity diminishes toward the end of the century, or at least is expressed in a freer mode. Artists in the years around 1700 share a lighter spirit, a silvery tone, a new elegance, and a more rational structure of form: Maratta was one of the first in Rome to discover this new style, but one finds it expressed also in Foggini's *Studies* and in Ghezzi's amusing *Caricatures*. These works mark the end of the period represented in our exhibition.

The Steiners' collection of Northern art is less extensive than the Italian one, but here again most periods of Flemish and Dutch art from about the middle of the sixteenth century onward can be illustrated with important works. The boisterous *Peasant Banquet* given to Marten van Cleve, for instance, is a rare and interesting example of the new genre scenes, best known from the paintings by Pieter Brueghel the Elder, created by the Renaissance in the North. Marten van Heemskerck's *Triumph of Christ* is the Dutch counterpart to the art of Vasari and Bronzino in Italy. This style is usually termed "Romanism" for its blatant imitation of Italian forms, yet here, in a flickering light evoking rich and mobile textures, strong emotion unites with a sense for the ornamental to create a uniquely fantastic and original work. Marten de Vos's Flemish contribution to the same tradition, the *Emperor Ninus*, is somewhat later and therefore more elegant and abstract in conception, not unlike the work of Trotti and della Rovere in the Italian section. But the dynamic stream of life flowing expressively through the emperor's body from head to toe is as typically Flemish as the light that evokes rich sensual surface on all the forms, even within this highly ornamental structure.

Landscapists like Tobias Verhaecht, represented in two key drawings in the Steiner Collection, were also inspired by encounters with Italy. Yet they succeed in creating dynamic evocations of the cosmic forces in nature, quite different in spirit from their Southern counterparts. Still, the abstract and geometric patterning remains typical of the art of the late sixteenth century. Like the Carracci, Jacob de Gheyn and Bloemaert begin to discover a new life, even though it is more difficult for them to break away from the predominance of formal structures and linear beauty so important to the sixteenth century. Their results are perhaps an even deeper penetration into the sensuous world and into personal emotions than that achieved by the Italians.

In the Netherlands the true revolution of the seventeenth century is carried through. Some of this can be felt in the *Study of a Head* by Rubens, where emotional intensity is combined with brilliant observation of skin and hair, or in the delicate evocation of evening light reflected on the silvery bark and leaves of poplars seen in Lucas van Uden's study of trees. This unique sense for the life forces in things comes out perhaps most brilliantly in the *Studies of Hounds* by David Teniers the Younger, where the animals are portrayed in all different positions. The artist's light stroke gives them mobility and grace, humorously concentrating on the pointed elegance of their tiny heads.

In Holland the light will not stay on the surface, but penetrates more deeply into the personal being and feelings of the people. In a work like Tengnagel's *Abraham Visited by the Angels* we can see the artist struggling to show us, with a minimum of movement and gesture, the great emotion of the patriarch at receiving the message. Saftleven's *Country Woman* sits still on her chair, but in her quiet pose and the features so lightly evoked by a few touches of grey and black chalk, we experience a whole life. In the same way, the concentrated occupation of the fishermen in Allaert van Everdingen's *River Landscape* helps us penetrate the peaceful and benevolent mood of this Dutch landscape, in which an old building slowly decomposes to become one with nature.

In Holland, too, there is a period when the emotions rise up and movement becomes more boisterous. Andries Both's *Artist Seated at His Easel* is a humorous, somewhat strident appeal to our sympathy for the poverty of the painter. In Rembrandt's art of the thirties this Baroque tendency to extreme expression finds its highest form and is passed on to his students. The dramatic light and gestures in Ferdi-

18

nand Bol's impressive drawing are perfect representatives of this style, as is the fierce countenance of the man in Govaert Flinck's *Portrait*.

The Steiners' interest in Dutch art has found a focus in the circle of Rembrandt, the artists inspired by this greatest of Dutch masters: Philips Koninck, the artist of *The Zaagmoelenpoort*, is one of them. In this highly impressive depiction of the dikes and windmills in the countryside around Amsterdam, water and plains mix with the ever moving sky to form an impression of geometric clarity of structure that later inspired Daubigny and Mondrian.

Another of Rembrandt's disciples was Roelant Roghman. In his *Wooded River Landscape* man becomes small among the grand trees through which the sun is shining, and yet feels a sense of intimacy and serenity. Lambert Doomer, the author of *Rebecca and Eliezer at the Well*, was also touched by the great man from Leyden. He boasts his knowledge of Rhenish castles and oriental animals while telling his story in a typically Dutch, down-to-earth manner, arousing our curiosity about far-off lands and times.

The Steiners' latest acquisition crowns and focuses this part of their collection. *Nathan Admonishing David* by Rembrandt is a classical work of around 1650, composed of only the simplest forms and lines. And yet, within this formal restraint—what depth of emotion! Hearing the quiet but deeply penetrating words of the prophet, David is startled and greatly moved. An inner drama is taking place, quite unlike the outer drama in Castiglione's *Crucifixion* of precisely the same date. The evolution of Dutch art culminates in the middle of the seventeenth century in the work of Rembrandt and a few other artists. The Steiner drawing is a perfect expression of the art of this moment.

In Holland, too, the seventeenth century ends on a lighter, more elegant note. Another star of the Steiner collection is the small but perfectly composed *Frigate at Anchor* of Willem van de Velde II. In silvery light and misty tone, humid clouds cover the quiet mirroring sea. Smoke rises from a salute that has been fired to honor the yacht in the background. Barges move between the larger vessels. Yet all man's activity is only one part of the calm mood that pervades water and sky.

No wonder that working with the Steiner drawings was exciting for the Harvard students who were lucky enough to do so. The collection is in fact much larger than what we are able to show for limitations of space and time. Choosing from the many treasures was one of the tasks that was highly educative for both students and editor. We wanted not only to find the works of the highest quality, but also to give the viewer the best possible survey of the two centuries here presented. Every museum curator's perpetual problem of choice was in this case faced by fresh eyes and minds.

Selection was only one aspect of the learning experience. The Steiners and their collections opened a new world to the students: drawings, this rich and wonderful field that can lead in so many directions. A sheet of studies is never a self-contained entity. One looks for others like it to reconstruct the artist's train of thought, or one searches for the finished work, the painting, sculpture, or building that grew out of the sketches. Two centuries of human culture became alive and assumed more concrete form.

There was yet a third dimension to our study: the personal and highly interesting world of the collector, the motives behind his purchases, his attachment to the works, the aesthetic predilections determining his choice, his philosophy, and cultural background. Here the students penetrated into the fertile ground where new trends and ideas germinate. Some of the most exciting parts of the course work were the visits to private collectors in the New York and Boston areas. Although each collector is clearly different from all the others and acts in a very distinct way, some patterns seemed to emerge and began to catch our imagination. The Steiners too fitted into a wider context.

Although latecomers in the field, the Steiners are part of a very special group of highly educated, kind, and generous collectors who have come to this country from Germany, Austria, and the region of the old Austro-Hungarian empire. The impact of these people on collecting and on the study of drawings in the United States can not be overstated. After a few visits to major private drawings collections in the New York area, my students began to believe that collecting was synonymous with Old World warmth and good cooking, especially of delicious sweets. This was an extra benefit none of us would have wanted to miss.

We want to thank the Steiners most warmly for their patience. They not only presented us with their beautiful drawings and let us choose the ones we most wanted to show, they provided us with precious information, often the result of much research in libraries on their part or of correspondence with scholars all over the world; and they also gave us the freedom to express our opinions about their treasures, even when our views did not fully coincide with theirs.

In the course of research for this project, numerous people have contributed valuable information and advice, only part of which we have been able to acknowledge in the catalogue proper. We would like to name them here with gratitude: George Abrams, Noel Annesley, the late Curtis Baer, Alessandro Ballarin, Jacob Bean, Egbert Haverkamp-Begemann, Alessandro Bettagno, Per Bjurström, James Burke, Bernice Davidson, Ebria Feinblatt, John Gere, Julius Held, R. A. d'Hulst, Lorna Lowe, Denis Mahon, Michael Mahoney, Manuela Mena Marqués, Mary Meyers, Mary Newcome, Edward J. Olszewski, Terisio Pignatti, Philip Pouncey, I. Q. van Regteren Altena, Frank Robinson, Herward Roettgen, Frederick Schab, Kaethe Schaeffer, Janos Scholz, Hugh Craig Smyth, Felice Stampfle, the late Wolfgang Stechow, Julien Stock, Bertina Suida Manning, Ann

Sutherland Harris, Werner Sumowski, Yvonne Tan-Bunzl, Peter Ward Jackson, Wolfgang Wegner, Emile Wolf, and Christopher Wright.

Equally valuable was the help we received from scholars and members of the staff at the Fogg Art Museum. Foremost amongst our helpers were Marjorie B. Cohn and her assistants, who checked the condition, medium, and inscription of every drawing and gave advice to the students on all technical problems, and also provided mats and frames to drawings which needed them. Seymour Slive and William Robinson checked out problems with Dutch drawings, and the latter was in fact our advisor on Northern art throughout the course. We often had recourse to Sydney Freedberg for Italian High Renaissance and *Maniera* problems. Our editor Janet Cox overcame unique odds in bringing together this multiplicity of efforts. Laura Giles practically camped out at the Fogg in order to tie up loose ends of all sorts and type the manuscript. Scott Schaefer was kind enough to read the final copy, and he and Meg Morgan helped with bibliography research. If the catalogue has any beauty it is thanks to Stephen Harvard and his colleagues at The Stinehour Press, and to Meriden Gravure.

The exhibition could never have taken place without the organizational help of Debby Wye, Suzannah Doeringer, and Jane Watts and her staff in the Registrar's office. It was installed at the Fogg with great professional care under the supervision of Laurence Doherty by Joao Tavares DeMelo and Adalino Mota. We wish to thank them all.

KONRAD OBERHUBER

NOTE TO THE CATALOGUE

Catalogue entries are arranged alphabetically by artist in two sections: Italian Drawings and Northern Drawings. All measurements are in millimeters; all paper is antique laid paper. Descriptions of watermarks refer to Edward Heawood, *Watermarks*, Monumenta Chartae Papyraceae, vol. 1 (Hilversum, Holland, 1950); and C. M. Briquet, *Les Filigranes, Dictionnaire historique des Marques du papier*, 4 vols. (Leipzig, 1923). References for all sales catalogues are included under PROV (provenance); references listed under BIBL in the technical paragraph preceding each entry indicate sources, if any, where the work has been published or discussed previous to this catalogue. These and notes in the text use author-date abbreviations to refer to the Bibliography following the Catalogue. The abbreviations "L." and "L. Suppl." refer to Frits Lugt, *Les Marques de collections de dessins & d'estampes* (Amsterdam, 1921), and its supplement volume (The Hague, 1956).

Each entry is initialed by its author.

A.A.	*Ann J. Adams*	M.M.	*Margaret P. Morgan*
E.B.	*Emily D. Bilski*	N.N.	*Nancy D. Netzer*
S.C.	*Susan J. Cooke*	K.O.	*Konrad Oberhuber*
P.F.	*Peter C. Freeman*	W.W.R.	*William W. Robinson*
N.H.	*Nicole Harris*	C.R.S.-S.	*Charles R.*
J.J.	*Joseph A. Jozlin*		*Saumarez-Smith*
A.K.	*Andrea E. Kaliski*	C.S.	*Cynthia Schneider*
L.K.	*Lesley Koenig*	T.S.	*Thomas R. Sylvester*
R.M.	*Richard Milhender*	R.Z.	*Rebecca Zurier*

1

ITALIAN DRAWINGS

Fra Bartolommeo della Porta
Savignano 1472 – Florence 1517

1 Drapery Study for a Standing Male Figure

280 x 152. Black chalk with white highlights; light brown (prepared?) paper. INSCR, black chalk, 16th-century hand: *del Frate*; verso: *di mano di / Fra Bartolomeo*; brown ink, upper edge 18th-century secondary support: *N⁰. 519*; upper center, inscription partially deleted: *Fra Bartolomeo / Fiorentino— / Mori d'anni 48 nel 1517.—*; graphite, center: *No. II*; lower l. corner: encircled *39*. PROV: unknown Italian collection; Erasmus Philipps, ca. 1730; H. M. Calmann (see L. Suppl. 2687)

Fra Bartolommeo was one of the first and most important Florentine masters of the High Renaissance. He quickly emancipated himself from his Quattrocento teacher Cosimo Rosselli and came under the spell of Leonardo. Bartolommeo's early pen and ink drawings, for which he sometimes prepared the paper with the tip of the brush loaded with diluted ink, possess extraordinary charm and lightness of touch. After trips to Venice and Rome in 1514 his technique became more painterly and his forms more monumental and grand.

His late works have been the subject of little study since von der Gabelentz (1922). This drawing would seem to date from somewhere between the 1509 altarpiece *Madonna with Saints Stephen and John the Baptist* in Lucca, with its slender, contrapuntal sharpness (Freedberg, 1971, pl. 255), and the fuller, more dynamic classicism of the figures in Andrea del Sarto's *Adoration of the Magi*, 1511, in the Pitti Palace. Might it be connected with Soderini's contemporary commission for an altar panel in the Sala del Gran Consiglio in the Palazzo Vecchio? According to Vasari, this panel was to depict "all the surviving saints of the city of Florence and those saints on whose days the city won its victories" (Vasari-Milanesi, 1880, IV, 199; Wind, 1944, pp. 233–243, for discussion of context). Though the

Steiner drawing can be related to no figure in the surviving under-painting (Freedberg, 1971, pl. 263), it has something of the militant piety that Soderini and Prior Pagnini were reviving at the time.

Drapery was always an important element in Fra Bartolommeo's expressive vocabulary; he developed it from billowing forms in a first draft into sculptural solidity in his paintings. Here he takes the full sweep of the cloak over the shoulder from a figure in a much earlier *Coronation of the Virgin* (Venturi, 1925, fig. 163) and renders it with an impressive rhythmic swirl.   C.R.S.-S.

Stefano della Bella
Florence 1610–1664

2   Sheet of Small Figure Studies

117 x 171. Graphite, pen and brown ink; off-white paper. PROV: Giuseppe Vallardi (L. 1223); William Mayor (L. 2779); Christie's, July 4, 1972, no. 75 (ill.); Lorna Lowe, Nov.–Dec. 1973, pl. 1

Stefano della Bella was a prolific printmaker whose numerous etch-ings of diminutive figures are in the tradition of Jacques Callot, whom he emulated in his youth. Born in Florence, Stefano trained first as a goldsmith, then as a draughtsman, and studied etching under Callot's former colleague Remigio Cantagallina. He went to Rome where he continued to work on illustrated court scenes for the Medici, and it was there that his style came into its own as he moved away from Callot's mannered poses and stylized execution toward a more spontaneous and natural expression. In Rome he developed the habit of sketching landscape and genre scenes from life (in the tradi-tion of the Dutch *Bamboccianti*) and subsequently used this material for figures and backgrounds in his prints. Della Bella moved to Paris in 1639, where he designed theatrical productions and fire-works, and a set of playing cards for the young Louis XIV.

The gracefully suggestive style of the Steiner drawing as well as the costumes identify it as a study sheet from della Bella's Parisian years (another group in the Louvre is discussed in Viatte, 1974, nos. 102–111, 224–226, and 244–249). Many of the figures corre-spond to the types shown in his etchings. The foreground group and the woman picking up her skirts in the upper right corner appear to

26

be related to the large print entitled *Le Pont Neuf à Paris*, published in 1646 (DeVesme, 1971, p. 175, no. 850). Especially close to this etching is the woman serving food from a basket to a group of children. The figure on horseback near the top of the sheet is similar to one in the background of a small traveling scene (ibid., p. 52, no. 195), while the cavaliers are related, though not as closely, to city and traveling scenes in two series entitled *Agréable Diversité de Figures* (ibid., p. 39, nos. 118 and 119) and *Diversi Capricci* (ibid., p. 42, nos. 135 and 137). R.Z.

Agnolo di Cosimo Tori, called *Bronzino*
Florence 1503–1572

3 Study of a Male Nude

239 x 460. Black chalk; off-white paper; upper corners and tips of lower corners clipped diagonally. INSCR, graphite, lower r. corner: *Angelo Bronzino*; verso 19th-century mounting: *No. 9*. PROV: Christie's, Dec. 9, 1975, no. 16

This drawing, first published in the Christie's sale as a work by Angelo Bronzino and approved as such by Craig Smyth, is a study for the figure in the bottom right of Bronzino's *Martyrdom of Saint Lawrence*—a Michelangelesque river god clasping an upturned urn. The fresco, commissioned by Cosimo de' Medici in 1565 to complete a cycle begun by Pontormo, is one of Bronzino's last works and represents the summit of the High *Maniera*, "a beautifully artificial fusion of gymnasium and ballet, played upon an antique stage" (Freedberg, 1971, p. 315). Each figure is isolated and the fresco built up by aggregate. The figure in the Steiner drawing, though highly finished, had to be considerably adapted. The urn was moved forward so that the twisted body might form the corner of the composition; the eyes were made to stare out with rhetorical anxiety; the shoulders were broadened and the rhythms simplified. The changes may explain why this drawing, unlike the other surviving studies (Louvre, inv. 10900, and Uffizi, inv. 10220; Smyth, 1971, fig. 40), is unsquared: Bronzino was still experimenting with the figure's torsion and was as yet uncertain in his outline.

4

Berenson (1938, I, p. 321) condemned Bronzino's draughtsmanship and Janet Cox-Rearick maintains that his imagination ossified at the end of his career (1971, p. 22, ". . . his refinement became academic, his line slapdash and less supple . . ."). This sheet, however, with its smooth sculptural surfaces and expressive vitality, vindicates and clarifies his late drawing style.   c.r.s.-s.

Luca Cambiaso
Moneglia 1527 – Madrid 1585

4   Annunciation

209 x 205. Pen and brown ink with grey and brown wash; white paper; top and bottom r. corners missing, lined, 18th-century mount. INSCR, brown ink, top r.: *Bellissima.* PROV: Sotheby's, Nov. 25, 1971, no. 146 (ill.); C. G. Boerner, Aug. 1972, no. 10 (ill.). BIBL: Nielson, 1972, no. 10

In this drawing, Luca Cambiaso brilliantly displays the Genoese preference for structural abstraction. Encouraged by his father, a second-rate *maniera* painter, Cambiaso assiduously studied local *maniera* examples by Pordenone, Perino del Vaga, and Giulio Romano. His paintings temper Roman plasticity with a distinctly Correggiesque light. But Luca's fame—in his own time as well as today —derives from his virtuoso draughtsmanship, particularly in his illusionistic foreshortenings and dramatic wash.

This drawing is a study for a painting in the Church of S. Annunziata di Portorio in Genoa (Suida Manning and Suida, 1958, fig. 234). Antonio di Franchi commissioned the work in the name of Battista Grimaldi on December 24, 1568, for fifty *scudi*. Bertina Suida Manning and Wilhelm Suida (ibid., pp. 39–40) and Robert Manning (1968, p. 21) have published drawings related to this painting. In an unpublished paper presented to the College Art Association in February, 1977, Edward J. Olszewski gives an even more complete account of these drawings, discussing fourteen studies related to the S. Annunziata painting. He suggests that several of these may have been studio copies executed by members of the Cambiaso workshop. Cambiaso is known to have experimented with his compositions; the numerous studies show changes in the

31

position of the angel and the expression of the Virgin. The Steiner *Annunciation*, by the master's own hand, is closest to the painting, except for its less vertical emphasis. The drawing may have been trimmed for its eighteenth-century mount, and that would account for the difference. The clipped corners indicate that the drawing was at one time pasted into an album.   A.K.

Domenico Campagnola
Venice 1500 – Padua 1564

5   Virgin and Child with Saints Michael and
Jerome in a Landscape

318 x 274. Pen and brown ink, black chalk underdrawing, some abrasions; brownish paper, made up on top r. and at l. and with tears lower l. and center, laid down. PROV: Sir Peter Lely (L. 2092); Prosper Henry Lankrinck (L. 2090); Hugh Squire, Sotheby's, July 4, 1975, no. 16; P. & D. Colnaghi. BIBL: Oberhuber, 1976, no. 57

Domenico Campagnola, born of German parents in Venice, was adopted by the famous Paduan engraver Giulio Campagnola, who also became his first teacher. The influence of Palma Vecchio—and later, Titian—was critical in Domenico's development as an artist. His was a very precocious talent, as a large number of his engravings and woodcuts are dated 1517 and 1518, and many of his drawings must have been created even earlier, when he was sixteen and seventeen years old. Many of these earliest drawings are, in fact, among the most exciting works in his oeuvre and show with what intensity the young artist absorbed the major artistic achievements of his time.

The Steiner drawing belongs to this period. Composition and style link it closely to his engraving *Virgin and Child with Saints* of 1517 (Hind, 1938–1948, v, 212, no. 8; Oberhuber, 1973, no. 154). Another early drawing of a *Sacra Conversazione* of this same type is now in the Ecole des Beaux-Arts in Paris (inv. 312; Tietze and Tietze-Conrat, 1944, no. 551 [ill.]; Oberhuber, 1973, p. 424); its style is somewhat freer and more advanced. The Steiner sheet is more finished and shows Domenico's typical dense cross-hatching

5

with its rich variability evoking a flickering light. The figures are expressively united by a diagonal movement from right to left, a dynamic drive which adds new life to similar representations by his contemporaries, such as the *Virgin Enthroned with Saint George and Saint Lucy* in S. Stefano in Vicenza, painted by Palma Vecchio (Mariacher, 1968, pl. 33).   K.O.

Remigio Cantagallina
Borgo San Scpolcro (?) 1582/83 – Florence 1656

6   View of a Tuscan Villa

270 x 404. Pen and brown ink over black chalk; white paper. INSCR, pen and ink, top center: *PCG* (in monogram) *a di 27 maggio 1624/f.* PROV: A. Mouriau (L. 1853); Charles Gasc (L. 543); Sotheby's, June 8, 1972, no. 40

Remigio Cantagallina was already respected as a landscape artist in the early seventeenth century. He was a student of Giulio Parigi, and collaborated with his better-known contemporary, Jacques Callot. Like his master, Cantagallina rarely painted, but concentrated on the graphic arts. In addition to Parigi, he was strongly influenced by Paul Brill, the most celebrated Northern landscape artist in early seventeenth-century Italy. Cantagallina himself traveled to the Netherlands in 1612 and 1613 (Chiarini, 1975, pp. 228–230).

This finished and signed drawing is in the style of the artist's etchings, characterized by the frequent use of parallel horizontal lines, particularly in the shrubbery and shadows. The line varies greatly, however, ranging from the short, heavy strokes in the foreground trees to a very light indication of distant detail in the background to the right. The date of 1624 and the clear and static composition with soft light place this drawing at an intermediate stage in Cantagallina's development. Earlier drawings like the *Saint Francis Receiving the Stigmata* of 1615 in the Janos Scholz Collection (Roli, 1969, no. 97) show stronger contrasts of light and shade, and more abstract structure of space and line in the style of Callot. These elements have been modified and softened in the Steiner sheet but the artist has not yet approached the naturalistic attention to detail, supported by both

35

7

line and wash, that appears in the *Village Piazza* of 1633, in the Princeton University Art Museum (ibid., no. 98).   T . S .

Annibale Carracci
Bologna 1560 – Rome 1609

7   Venus in Clouds, Holding a Mirror

165 x 228, irregular. Black chalk with pinkish chalk, pen and brown ink with touches of brown wash, heightened with touches of white and pink gouache; grey-blue paper; laid down, upper r. corner made up with second piece of darker blue paper, parts of r. and l. edges repaired. INSCR, graphite, verso: *AnnCaracci*. PROV: J. E. Pryde, Fife, Scotland; Sotheby's, June 27, 1974, no. 32 (ill.)

Annibale Carracci was the most talented and influential member of the remarkable family of Bolognese artists which included his brother Agostino and their cousin Lodovico. In his Roman works, and especially in the Farnese Gallery frescoes, Annibale created a new type of illusionist decoration, and set the standard for the classical style of seventeenth-century European painting.

This stunning drawing of Venus is neither recorded in the Carracci literature nor related to any known paintings or compositions. However, the attribution confirmed orally by Jacob Bean is further supported by evidence from other Annibale sheets. Although the combination of chalks, gouache, and pen and ink seldom appears in Annibale's drawings, the pen work and the handling of the chalks compare well with several drawings dating from around 1590: the Madrid and Uffizi studies (Posner, 1971, pls. 46b and c) for the Madrid *Venus and Adonis*, and two drawings, now at Windsor, connected with the *Founding of Rome* decorations in the Palazzo Magnani, Bologna (ibid., pls. 52d and n).

By 1587 Annibale had already been exposed to the art of Venice and Parma, but not until 1595 did he go to Rome, where he witnessed the monumentality and grandeur of the Roman tradition. From then on his drawings were importantly influenced by the Roman style.

Earlier drawings such as the *Study for a Dead Christ* in the Uffizi

37

and the *Study of St. Louis* in Berlin (ibid., pls. 24b and 41d) are not yet as powerfully plastic or subtly modeled as the *Venus*. On the other hand, figure studies made in Rome for the Farnese Gallery decorations (see Martin, 1965) are far more monumental, with greater articulation of the musculature and a very different quality of light and modeling.

The wide hips and rounded, protruding stomach of the Steiner Venus are further clues to the date of the drawing. Similar female nudes appear in such paintings as the Madrid *Venus and Adonis* and the Washington *Toilet of Venus* of about 1594 (ibid., pls. 46a and 85).

M.M.

Lodovico Carracci
Bologna 1555–1619

8 Return of the Prodigal Son

274 x 202. Pen and brown ink, brown wash, over black chalk; buff paper; small losses lower r. edge and corners, lined. INSCR, black ink, verso of lining sheet: *Ecole 225 d'Anibale Carracci N7* (*225* and *N7* struck out; *Ecole* and *d'* in different ink); green crayon: *5*; graphite: *6*. PROV: Sotheby's, March 21, 1974, no. 12 (ill.)

Lodovico Carracci and his younger cousins, Agostino and Annibale, led the movement toward greater expressiveness and naturalism in Bolognese painting at the end of the sixteenth century.

The Carracci are known to have collaborated on designs for fresco decorations, and possibly easel paintings, during the period they worked together in Bologna. The Steiner drawing, although certainly by Lodovico, is very similar in composition to drawings by Agostino at Windsor Castle (Wittkower, 1952, nos. 95 and 96 verso) and the Uffizi (inv. 3798s; Posner, 1971, II, fig. 54). Another sheet at Windsor (Wittkower, 1952, no. 96 recto) and one at the Louvre (inv. 7353) show studies by Agostino for individual figures in this composition.

A slightly different version of the theme, at Chatsworth (inv. 434), may be a copy after a drawing by Annibale (Holland, 1961, no. 165), although Wittkower attributes it also to Agostino (Wittkower, 1952, no. 95). No painting by Lodovico of the Prodigal Son is

38

8

known to exist, although in 1631 there was one by him listed as being in the Dulcini Gallery in Bologna (Bodmer, 1939, p. 139). The drawings by Lodovico and Agostino correspond to an engraving in the *Galerie du Palais d'Orléans* (no. 9), after a lost painting attributed to Annibale in the early literature (see Wittkower, no. 95, and Posner, 1971, I, 162, n. 32).

The attribution of this drawing to Lodovico is based on the linear economy and decorative grace of the draughtsmanship and the subtle use of washes to strengthen the design and suggest form, all characteristic of his drawings of the early 1590s (see Bodmer, 1934, pp. 53–54). The style of the *Prodigal Son* is similar to that of a drawing by Lodovico in the Metropolitan Museum of Art (Stampfle and Bean, 1967, no. 4), which may be related to Agostino's painting of the *Last Communion of St. Jerome* in the Bologna Pinacoteca (Bologna, 1956, no. 39 [ill.]; there dated 1593 or 1594).   s.c.

Domenico-Maria Canuti
Bologna 1620–1684

9   Seated Prophet and Another Study of His Head

210 x 169 irregular. Pen and brown ink, sanguine and brown washes over red chalk; verso, red chalk; buff paper. INSCR, graphite, verso, lower l.: *661 del V. Cenuto*; illegible inscr. l. of base of tree. PROV: Joseph Klein, New York, Sotheby's, Oct. 10, 1974, no. 41, pl. 2
Verso: Man Seated behind a Tree

A student and follower of Guido Reni, Canuti was long neglected and virtually forgotten by art historians. Through the work of Ebria Feinblatt and others, however, his art and artistic personality have begun to take shape and his oeuvre has been partially reconstructed (Feinblatt, 1952; Feinblatt, 1961; Poensgen, 1967). Canuti worked in both Bologna and Rome and earned his reputation principally in ceiling decorations of Biblical and mythological subjects. He also made wall frescoes and casel paintings (Benezit, 1976, pp. 502–503).

As Ebria Feinblatt has noted in correspondence, the drawing in the Steiner Collection (one of the few by Canuti in the United States) may be connected with the figure representing the Melan-

9

10

cholic Humor in the *Four Temperaments* in S. Michele in Bosco, Bologna. As she further points out, however, the pose in the final fresco is considerably altered. Other studies for the same figure in Besançon and the Janos Scholz Collection (Feinblatt, 1961, figs. 7–10) suggest that Canuti's original plans for the figure developed in a different direction from that indicated by the Steiner study.

Miss Feinblatt also notes that the pose of the Steiner figure echoes in reverse the pose of a Prophet Hosea by Raphael in his decorations for S. Maria della Pace in Rome (Dussler, 1966, pp. 103–105, no. II-9). The reversal of the Raphael pose suggests that Canuti knew it through a print, but it is possible that he consciously and freely adapted the pose of the Raphael in reverse for his own purposes.

The charming, whimsical red chalk sketch on the verso shows a tree trunk with an artist seated behind it, with only the sides of his broad back visible.   M.M.

Giovanni Benedetto Castiglione
Genoa 1600 – Mantua 1663

10   Crucifixion with Saints and God the Father

>401 x 274. Brush and brown oil paint with blue, red, and white touches; cream paper; creased, gold line painted about 3 mm. from edge at a later date. PROV: Benjamin West (L. 419); private collection, England; Thos. Agnew & Sons Ltd., London. BIBL: Percy, 1971, no. 54 (ill.); Edinburgh, 1972, no. 29 (ill.); Metropolitan Museum, 1976

Now recognized as one of the great draughtsmen of the seventeenth century, Castiglione received his early training in Genoa and may well have studied with van Dyck there between 1621 and 1627 (Percy, 1971, p. 24). The art of the Flemish master had a profound effect on Castiglione throughout his career; it was probably in an attempt to achieve the effect of the oil sketches of van Dyck and Rubens that he devised his technique of drawing on paper with a fine brush dipped first in oil, and then in dry, unbound pigment. During a stay in Rome in the 1630s he adopted compositional ideas from Poussin and probably encountered the work of Pietro Testa. By the time of his second visit to Rome (1647–1651), Castiglione was using the brush technique to make elaborately finished colored drawings which were not studies for other works but which explored independently the religious and allegorical themes which he was also treating in paintings, etchings, and monotypes. While in Rome he began to incorporate the Baroque fervor of Bernini into his style.

The Steiner drawing belongs to a series of Crucifixion scenes which Blunt assigns to the period 1655–1660 because of their high degree of finish and use of color (Blunt, 1954, pp. 40–41). While he has argued that these were personal meditations on the theme of the passion (ibid., p. 21), most of the figures correspond, albeit freely, to those depicted in traditional accounts. This drawing follows the theme of the Swoon of the Virgin which Réau (1955–1959, II, 499) traces back to the end of the Middle Ages, and includes the Virgin, Saint John, and Mary Magdalene. There is no literary precedent for the presence of God the Father supported by angels, a group which Castiglione frequently added to scenes of this type.

Though the series is usually isolated by historians from the rest of the artist's oeuvre, it shows a development which parallels the overall evolution of Castiglione's style after his return to Rome toward greater control of the medium and more concentrated dramatic vision. Ostrow (1968, pp. 27–29) has suggested one scheme for dating these Crucifixion scenes based on an internal development from simpler vertical compositions (as in the *Christ on the Cross* at Windsor, inv. 3959) to more complex horizontal scenes (Windsor, inv. 3894). But on the basis of stylistic comparison with the rest of Castiglione's work in these years a different development, in fact the reverse of that suggested by Ostrow, appears to be more plausible. The horizontal drawing at Windsor, in its van Dyckian "soft" brushwork and heavy modeling of forms and its Testa-like grotesque, elongated figures, recalls earlier brush drawings such as *Christ Preaching to the Apostles* (Percy, 1971, fig. 18) which date from the beginning of Castiglione's second visit to Rome. The artist's more mature style is drier and less tightly modeled; his compositions are simpler as in the *Christ on the Cross* at Windsor (inv. 3959) and the preparatory sketch for the *Immaculate Conception Adored by Saints Francis and Anthony of Padua* which Waterhouse has definitively dated to 1649–1650 (Waterhouse, 1967, p. 5).

44

The Steiner drawing would come slightly later than this, possibly 1651. It shows a further development of dramatic power, both in the strong diagonal composition and the sense of Baroque ecstasy in the mood and the turbulent drapery. The influence of Bernini is seen especially in the figure of the Virgin, whose pose and expression recall his *Saint Theresa in Ecstacy*, which was being completed in Rome at this time. The drama of the scene is heightened by the Steiner drawing's unique view of Christ from behind. This appears to have been Castiglione's own invention, though van Dyck painted a Crucifixion scene in which one of the thieves is seen from the same angle (Boymans–van Beuningen Museum, inv. 2517).   R.Z.

Giuseppe Cesari, called *Cavaliere d'Arpino*
Arpino 1568 – Rome 1640

11   Head of a Bearded and Hooded Man

260 x 160. Pen and brown ink; cream paper; stains, irregular edges cut down from a larger drawing and mounted in full on a secondary sheet. INSCR: *Gioseppino d'Arpino; 24*; verso of mount: *33*; probably in a modern hand: *d'Aspini*. PROV: L'Art Ancien

The son of an impoverished painter, Giuseppe Cesari left Arpino for Rome in 1582. He remained there most of his life, with the exception of several years in Naples following 1589, when he went to work in the church of S. Martino ai Monti. Cesari quickly became a popular and highly respected artist, patronized by both Pope Gregory XIII and Clement VIII. Although he was the teacher of Caravaggio (1573–1610) for several years, Cesari avoided the early Baroque style of his pupil and remained one of the last late mannerist artists in Italy. He is probably best known for his easily read, ornamental battle and religious scenes in fresco.

Herward Roettgen and Ann Sutherland Harris first attributed this drawing to Cesari. Roettgen suggested in correspondence that this head represents a priest, and may be a study for one of Cesari's last frescoes, *The Investiture of the Vestal Virgins*, 1639–1640, in the Palazzo dei Conservatori in Rome. The drawing is exceptional because Cesari seldom drew with pen and ink at the end of his life.   L.K.

Giuseppano d'arpa

11

Giovanni Battista Foggini
Florence 1652–1725

12 Designs for Architecture and Sculpture

296 x 214. Pen and brown ink over black chalk; cream paper; damage along l. edge, upper and lower corners replaced, vertical crease at center, watermark: paschal lamb with flag. INSCR, graphite, upper r. corner: *4*; brown ink, upper l.: *40*

$$\frac{70}{11.0}$$

PROV: Luca Beltrami; Sotheby's, July 9, 1973, no. 74 (as Johann Paul Schor [ill.]); Yvonne Tan-Bunzl. BIBL: Beltrami, 1916, no. 9; Monaci, 1974

Verso: Black chalk sketch for side of a catafalque

Giovanni Battista Foggini was the most important sculptor in Florence during the final half-century of Medici rule. As first sculptor and architect to the court of Grand Duke Cosimo III, his duties included supervising the ducal workshops and the design of decorative arts for the court.

The Steiner sheet is similar in size, format, and subject to drawings in the Metropolitan Museum of Art (Meyers, 1975, nos. 23–28) and in the vellum-bound volume in the Uffizi known as the *Giornale del Foggini* (inv. 8027A; pub. in Lankheit, 1959). The offprints on the recto and verso indicate that the drawing was probably once part of a volume similar to the *Giornale*.

Foggini frequently combined studies for different subjects on a single sheet. In the drawings on the recto he seems to deal with three separate projects: a church facade, a sculptural group of the Visitation, and an altar design. The putti with a hammer may be related to the latter, in which the Veil of Veronica and the cross and spear allude to the Passion.

On the verso is sketched one side of a catafalque, decorated with candles, consisting of a large obelisk at the top of a short flight of stairs flanked by two smaller obelisks. A similar catafalque is depicted on leaf 136 verso of the *Giornale* (Lankheit, 1959, p. 67, fig. 11) and another, with the obelisk raised over an arch, is drawn on a sheet in the Metropolitan (Meyers, 1975, no. 27 recto).

Lankheit connects the catafalque in the *Giornale* with the commemoration of the death in 1716 of the Elector Palatine Johann Wilhelm of the House of Wittelsbach, Grand Duke Cosimo's son-in-law and political ally. The catafalque in the Steiner drawing, however, lacks any identifying symbols which would link it definitely to these decorations. In addition, catafalque designs were often reused and rearranged for a variety of projects.

On stylistic evidence, Monaci dates the drawings on the recto to around 1723 (Monaci, 1974, pp. 58–59). A date late in the artist's career is further supported by the idiosyncratic handling of hair, drapery, and musculature in the Steiner sheet. These characteristics of Foggini's later style are also seen in a study he made for a bronze sculpture of *David and Goliath* executed in 1723 (Detroit-Florence, 1974, no. 12).   S. C.

Giovanni Battista Franco
Udine 1510 – Venice 1580

13   Design for the Decoration of an Apse

494 x 330. Brown pen and ink and grey wash over black chalk; white foxed paper; watermark: crowned *b* with cross, similar to Briquet no. 8090. INSCR, graphite, verso: *Raphael Urbino*. PROV: Chiltern Art Gallery

Although of Venetian origin, Battista Franco received his major training in Rome. He concentrated on drawing the major monuments of antiquity and the Renaissance, which he later published in etchings and engravings. His attempts at monumental composition were, however, severely criticized by his contemporaries for his failure to combine into a coherent whole the grand and expressive figures he so carefully selected, especially from the work of Michelangelo (Freedberg, 1971, p. 333). It was probably his lack of success in large-scale compositions in Rome that led Franco to seek a more provincial audience in Urbino, from where he later returned to Venice (Rearick, 1959, p. 111).

An awareness of his own shortcomings may have prompted the artist to break up a large wall space, such as that presented by the apse in this particular design, into a number of smaller compositions

13

representing scenes from the Passion and from the Life of the Virgin. One can see this course being followed in a later ceiling painting of *Virtues and Angels* in the Grimani Chapel in S. Francesco della Vigna in Venice, of 1561 (ibid., p. 123, fig. 10).

The Victoria and Albert Museum has a fragment of the same apse composition (inv. 97), which served as a preparatory drawing for the finished Steiner sheet; both are discussed in Peter Ward-Jackson's unpublished catalogue of the Victoria and Albert drawings, to which the author kindly allowed the Steiners access. Ward-Jackson uses the width of the door visible in the Steiner drawing at the base of the apse to calculate the approximate size of the project, concluding that it must have been intended for a large church and not for a side chapel.

As Ward-Jackson observes, the only commission on this scale with which Franco is known to have been involved is the Cathedral of Urbino, where he painted the *Assumption of the Virgin* on the dome in the Tribuna in 1545–1546, and also worked on the Chapel of the Sacraments in 1551 (Vasari-Gronau, 1904–1927, v, 133–134). Ward-Jackson suggests that the design of the apse could have been included in the original commission. Unfortunately, this section of the Cathedral collapsed in 1789, and Vasari offers no specifics on Franco's work there other than a description of the frescoes in the dome itself; the apse design seems never to have been executed. Additional information from the Archives of Urbino (ibid., v, 135, n. 25) indicates that there was a disagreement between the Duke of Urbino and Franco, which could have led to the abandonment of the project.

T.S.

Geronimo dai Paesi
Verona, active ca. 1580–1600

14   Jonah Deposited by the Whale

235 x 362. Pen and brown ink; white paper; glue residue (formerly mounted), watermark: anchor with ring in circle. INSCR, brown ink, lower r.: *Di Geronimo dai Paesi Veronese.* PROV: J. P. Heseltine (L. 1507, but not in circle); M. Komor (L. Suppl. 1882ᵃ)

Veronese landscape painting of the later sixteenth century has not yet received proper critical attention. The major artists of the period, such as Battista and Marco Angolo del Moro, Battista Pittoni, and Giovanni Battista Fontana, are best known for their etchings (Oberhuber, 1966, pp. 160–164). These reveal influences both from Venice and Padua, especially from Titian and Domenico Campagnola, but also from the art of the Netherlands.

The Steiner drawing is attributed by an old hand to a now unknown Veronese artist, Geronimo dai Paesi (literally, Jerome of the Landscapes). The work is clearly related to the Veronese school. Elements of the composition, a foreground ledge with trees and Jonah, the walled town with hills and castles beyond the water in the middleground, and the mountains rising from the sea in the distance, correspond well with a landscape print by Giovanni Battista Fontana (ibid., no. 272, fig. 41), inspired by Northern prototypes.

The figure group derives from two prints by Jan Sadeler after Dirck Barendsz., one of Titian's Dutch assistants: the whale is from *Jonah Spat Up by the Whale* (Judson, 1970, pl. 48), and the figure of Jonah is taken from the fourth figure from the right in *Mankind before the Flood* (ibid., pl. 41). While the whale is copied almost precisely, the artist reversed the figure and added the drapery. In the Sadeler print Jonah is crawling on hands and knees from the whale's mouth; here he is presented in a more dignified pose, facing the whale with an expression more proper to a prophet—at least in Italian eyes.

The Sadeler prints, engraved from designs by Barendsz. of 1582, help us date the Steiner drawing to the last years of the sixteenth century. It is to be hoped that this powerful sheet will provide a clue to the identification of further work by this interesting artist and lead to the discovery of his full name and biography.   P.F. and K.O.

Pier Leone Ghezzi
Rome 1674–1755

15   Caricatures of Four People

315 x 220. Pen and brown ink; cream paper; laid down on album page, with pale blue-green borders applied, restored loss upper r., watermark: encircled fleur de lis with *B* at base, surmounted by a

14

15

bird. INSCR, brown ink: *29*; on album page: (1) *Monsignor Cerri* (2) *La Sig.ra Manganoni*; verso: *709 K.* PROV: Carlos Bourbon, King of Naples (Charles III of Spain); Charles IV of Spain; Joseph Bonaparte; the first through seventh dukes of Wellington; R. M. Light & Co.

16 A Majordomo

338 x 192. Brown ink over black chalk; cream paper; laid down on album page with blue borders applied, restored loss upper l., restored tears upper center and lower center extending around foot. INSCR, brown ink, verso: *72-U12-CMLW, L,* encircled *D 227.* PROV: Herbert E. Feist Gallery

One of the most prominent figures in the artistic milieu of eighteenth-century Rome, Pier Leone Ghezzi held a secretarial position at the Accademia di San Luca and the office of papal painter from 1708 to 1747. Always a leader of fashion, he painted portraits of the aristocracy, frescoed their palaces, and directed decorating schemes (from festivals to coast guard boats) for the Pope. In addition, this remarkably prolific individual was an engraver of gems, an amateur musician, and an archeologist (Clark, 1974).

It is as the first professional caricaturist, however, that Ghezzi has always been best known. He produced over two thousand images of almost everyone obvious or eccentric enough to be noticed in Rome (Loret, 1935, p. 297). Caricature was particularly well suited to the irreverence of the eighteenth century where, as Abbé Lanzi remarked forty years after Ghezzi's death, "Freedom of the pencil was thought a desirable addition to license of the tongue" (Lanzi, 1796; p. 513 of 1852 edition).

Ghezzi's facility with the pen was encouraged at an early age. His father, Giuseppe, whose own creative energies were drained by the official duties imposed upon a prominent painter, had wanted Pier Leone to be a draughtsman. In spite of his father's caution, Pier Leone's own career followed that of Giuseppe. After the 1740s, Ghezzi's caricatures provided an outlet for personal statement in a life filled with official responsibilities (Clark, 1963, pp. 11–14).

Ghezzi's early brush burlesques and his subsequent style, using vertical lines in the manner of Callot, were replaced in the 1740s by more carefully wrought drawings of which the two Steiner carica-

16

tures are excellent examples. These are distinguished by light out-lines with regularly spaced hatchings, similar to an etching style. Ghezzi presumably used this technique to facilitate the transfer of the image to a copper plate at a future time, but only a small group of drawings were ever reproduced in this way.

During his lifetime, many of Ghezzi's caricatures were bound to-gether in volumes. The *Caricatures of Four People* comes from a set of three albums which can be traced to the court of Carlos Bourbon, King of Naples from 1734 to 1759. Four other drawings from these albums are at the Metropolitan Museum, New York (one recording an event of 1750–1751; Metropolitan Museum, 1976, nos. 20–23); a fifth, dated 1749, is owned by the Minneapolis Institute of Arts (Clark, 1974, p. 63, fig. 2). Our drawing depicts Monsignor Cerri (whose skull cap indicates a possible clerical position), La Signora Manganoni, and two other figures in conversation. The second drawing, *A Majordomo*, portrays a distinguished chief official of a princely household. Neither passionately satirical nor malicious, Ghezzi's caricatures record in good humor the colorful personalities of Roman society.　A.A.

Pietro Paolo Bonzi, called *Gobbo dei Carracci*
Cortona ca. 1576 – Rome 1636

17　Landscape with Castle

150 x 188. Pen and brown ink with graphite heightening; cream paper; laid down. INSCR, pen and brown ink, mostly abraded, verso, upper l.: — *ecole Lombarde / paysage – à la plume*; pen and black ink over graphite, below: *antonio Carracci da venetia 1583–1618 / Scuola Bononiana*; graphite, lower edge: *Domenico Zampieri 1581–1641 / gen. Domenichino.* PROV: Everard Jabach (L. Suppl. 2122c); unidentified collector's mark on verso: crossed swords; Parke-Bernet, New York, Oct. 22, 1970, no. 10 (ill.); Schaeffer Galleries

Formerly attributed to Domenico Zampieri, called Domenichino (1581–1641), the drawing is here given for the first time to a less well known member of the Carracci entourage, Pietro Paolo Bonzi, called Gobbo dei Carracci or Gobbo dei Frutti. Although the gen-eral appearance and type of the Steiner sheet are close to Domeni-

chino's landscapes such as the Windsor *Men Playing Skittles* and the Ashmolean *Saint Jerome* (Borea, 1965, pls. 10b and 57), the quality of the line and the articulation of the space are sufficiently different from his style to cause doubts about such an attribution. On the other hand, landscape drawings by Gobbo, which are very like Domenichino's in many ways (Chiarini, 1972, nos. 14–16), are remarkably similar to the Steiner sheet in all respects. One study in particular, also a *Castle in a Landscape* (Uffizi; ibid., no. 15), shows precisely the same delicate, sensitive line, feathery light foliage, and general construction of the forms as those found in the Steiner drawing, as well as a similar type of composition and articulation of the space. Its attribution to Gobbo is supported by two monogrammed landscape etchings by him (Battisti, 1954, figs. 11–12). The Steiner drawing can reasonably be given to him also.

Through the contemporary writings of Baglione (1733, p. 229) and the more recent articles of Hess and Battisti (1954), we know that Gobbo was principally a decorator (Palazzo Mattei; Battisti, 1954, figs. 4–7; Hess, 1954, fig. 3) and painter of fruit still lifes (e.g., Madrid; Battisti, 1954, figs. 1–2), who also drew and etched landscapes in the style of Annibale Carracci. Beyond these few facts, we have little substantiated information about his artistic education and his relationship to the Carracci school.   M.M.

Giovanni Francesco Barbieri, called *Il Guercino*

Cento 1591 – Bologna 1666

18   Seated Male Figure

275 x 285: Red chalk; very thin off-white paper; minor restorations along r. edge, watermark: shield containing a crown and an illegible device surmounted by a cardinal's hat, somewhat similar to Heawood 793. INSCR, graphite, verso, lower r.: *174576*; upper l.: *34*; brown ink: *P.* PROV: Sotheby's, Nov. 21, 1974, no. 49

Giovanni Francesco Barbieri, called Il Guercino ("the Squinter"), painted some of the most powerful works of the second decade of the seventeenth century. The two years (1621–1623) he spent in Rome working for Pope Gregory XV mark the turning point in his

18

career. After that time, he largely abandoned the Full Baroque style he had developed under the influence of works by Scarsellino and Lodovico Carracci, and turned increasingly toward the classicism of Guido Reni.

This magnificent study of a seated male figure and the head and shoulders of a second figure to the left belongs to Guercino's early period in Cento. Mahon dates the drawing about 1618–1619 and suggests that it may be a study for the *Raising of Lazarus*, probably painted in 1619 (Mahon, 1968, no. 35).

Guercino frequently proposed several very different compositional solutions for a painting in his preparatory drawings, which can make it difficult to assign a drawing to any one work.

From 1618 to 1619, Guercino was working on several paintings involving seated male figures, including the *Martyrdom of Saint Peter* in the Galleria Estense in Modena (ibid., no. 32), the *Lazarus*, and a lost painting of *Saint Sebastian Cured by the Women* known through several preparatory drawings (Mahon, 1969, nos. 41–43).

The figure in the Steiner drawing, whose pose and expression suggest a martyrdom, is most similar to a bound figure being attacked by a devil in a study which Mahon connects with the lost *Saint Sebastian* (ibid., no. 243). S.C.

19 Profile Portrait of a Man Wearing the Order of the Golden Fleece

172 x 147. Pen and brown ink; cream paper; partial watermark: *c.*
PROV: Sir Joshua Reynolds (L. 2364); P. O. Dubaut (L. 2103b); Pietro Scarpa, Venice

The cursory, fluid line of this rapid pen sketch contrasts strongly with the style of the red chalk *Seated Male Figure*, demonstrating another aspect of Guercino's remarkable draughtsmanship. Similar portraits, made either for the artist's own pleasure or for the entertainment of the sitter, abound in Guercino's work. They were often caricatures, a genre made popular by Agostino and Annibale Carracci. The Steiner sheet, while not a caricature, is closest in style to this group (Mahon, 1969, nos. 236 and 237). The Princeton *Head of a*

19

Pope (Bean, 1966, no. 44), a non-caricature sketch, can, however, be related to the Steiner portrait as well.

It is particularly difficult to date these drawings since Guercino's style remained remarkably consistent through the years, but the Steiner sheet most likely dates from the 1620s. Later drawings have a stronger, drier, more incisive character, while those of the twenties are more freely calligraphic and less rigidly controlled (ibid., nos. 42 and 43). Preparatory studies for early paintings such as the *Resurrection of Lazarus* and the *Investiture of Saint Julian* of 1619 and 1620 show a similar fluidity and freedom of line, as well as a like definition of forms (Mahon, 1967, nos. 44, 60, 69).

The sitter has not yet been identified satisfactorily. He resembles the coin profile images of Ferdinand Gonzaga, sixth duke of Mantua, 1587–1626, and his brother Vincenzo II, seventh duke of Mantua, 1594–1627 (Ambrosoli, 1906, no. 75; Panvini-Rosati, 1968, fig. 220). Neither brother, however, was ever honored with the Order of the Golden Fleece although both their father and another brother were members (*Toison d'Or*, 1904, nos. 283 and 318). No possessor of the Order who resembles the imposing figure in the Steiner drawing has yet been identified.   M.M.

Ottavio Leoni
Rome ca. 1580 – after 1632

20   Portrait of a Young Man

232 x 154. Black and red chalk with touches of white; faded paper; blue stain around edges. INSCR, lower l.: *18 Marco O*; center: *1632*.
PROV: William Schab Gallery, Oct. 23 – Dec. 3, 1972, Catalogue 52, no. 77

Leoni's seventeenth-century biographer Baglione (1733, p. 209) described his work as "so well done that in all of Rome there was no one who had not had his portrait done by Ottavio . . ." (tr. in Thomas, 1916, p. 328).

Though he remains best known for his series of engravings of notable Italians, the bulk of Leoni's work consists of hundreds of small bust-length portraits done in black and red chalk. Most of these were not studies for other works but finished drawings. The

18
Marco
o

1637

20

Portrait of a Young Man is typical of these portraits in three-quarter view, and shows Leoni's characteristic treatment of hair, which is at once free and detailed. The use of heavy lines around the mouth is found in many of Leoni's portraits such as the drawing of Gabriel Ciaberra in the Biblioteca Marucelliana in Florence (ibid., p. 368 [ill.]). Most of Leoni's chalk drawings were done on blue paper, and the stain along the edges of this sheet indicates that it may have originally been blue. Numerous *pentimenti* around the torso show that the artist changed the figure's pose and placement on the page at least once in the course of making the drawing.

Kruft (1969, p. 454) has shown by comparison with portraits by other artists that Leoni tended to idealize his subjects. This was consistent with contemporary aesthetic theories which advocated the "judicious" improvement of nature, taught at the Accademia di San Luca where Leoni was *Principe* in 1614.

The inscription in brown ink is similar to the dates and numerical codes found at the bottom of most of Leoni's chalk portraits. It is not known whether this spidery hand belonged to Leoni himself or to a later annotator. In this case the inscription is especially important, since writers disagree on the time of Leoni's death, some assuming a date as early as 1625–1626, others as late as 1638, or even 1659.

R.Z.

Giovanni Battista Trotti, called Il Malosso
Cremona 1555 – Parma 1619

21 The Three Magi

370 x 375. Pen and brown wash, squared in black chalk; white paper.
PROV: P. Sandby (L. 2112); Lorna Lowe, 1974, no. 43, pl. 12

Born in Cremona, Giovanni Battista Trotti lived all his life in Northern Italy. Studying with the Mannerist Bernardino Campi, he appears to have adapted his master's decorative and flickering contour lines to his own more dramatic expression. An interest in the interplay of light and volume, possibly the result of an early attraction to the art of Pordenone and Correggio, made Malosso more susceptible to the influence of the Bolognese school. Mario di Giam-

21

paolo notes that Cremonese drawing style was heavily influenced by Orazio Samacchini and singles out Malosso as an example (Giampaolo, *Antichità Viva*, 1974, p. 61).

Among published drawings by Trotti, the closest to the style of *The Three Magi* are an *Annunciate Angel* in the Uffizi and a *Mercury* sold at Sotheby's (March 6, 1973, no. 242), both dated by Giampaolo to around 1585–1590 (Giampaolo, *Arte Illustrata*, 1974, p. 21, figs. 33 and 38). Malosso's works prior to this period are more delicate and strongly influenced by Samacchini (ibid., figs. 4–10). The works after 1589 relinquish the sharp definition of masses and clear contrast of light, characteristics of the Steiner sheet, for a greater atmospheric effect and rhythmic unity of form (ibid., figs. 11, 12, 30).

The subject, possibly the Three Magi on their way to Bethlehem, is unusual for an oil painting and does not relate to any of Malosso's documented commissions.   A.K.

Carlo Maratta
Camerano 1626 – Rome 1713

22 Drapery Study of an Angel

407 x 269. Red chalk with white chalk highlights; blue paper; restored tear lower l. into torso of figure, lower l. corner missing and patched. INSCR, pen, lower l.: *31*. PROV: Christie's, March 30, 1976, no. 17 (ill.); Thos. Agnew and Sons, Ltd.

Carlo Maratta invested with new vigor the monumental yet simple plastic forms of his teacher Andrea Sacchi, and upon the deaths of Sacchi and Pietro da Cortona, he emerged as the leading painter of seventeenth-century Rome. Maratta executed many drapery studies, maintaining that they were equal in importance to studies of the figure.

This drawing is for one of the representations of the Archangel Gabriel, depicted in several versions of the *Annunciation* painted by Maratta and his studio. In its composition and the full forms of the drapery, it most closely relates to the version at Windsor Castle (Levey, 1964, no. 539), which is undated. Thus the Steiner drawing must be dated on stylistic grounds.

Manuela Mena Marqués has orally linked it to the early 1670s. Drawings of this period, such as two studies at Düsseldorf (FP 13741 and FP 13749, Sutherland Harris and Schaar, 1967, nos. 260 and 263) for the *Triumph of Clemency*, Palazzo Altieri, have moved beyond Maratta's early hard-surfaced drapery style which owed its complicated deep folds to the influence of Andrea Sacchi. Drawings of the 1670s define a soft, bulky surface over which light floats, without the twisted, vigorously falling folds of the late years. Sir Ellis Waterhouse rightly observes that the facial type of Maratta's Gabriel was modeled upon the left angel of Castiglione's *Immaculate Conception* now at the Minneapolis Institute of Arts (Waterhouse, 1967, p. 7). Francis Dowley points out that Gabriel's pose was inspired by Francesco Albani's *Annunciation* in Sta. Maria della Pace, Rome (Dowley, 1957, p. 171).

The Annunciation was a popular subject with Maratta and his studio. In addition to the painting at Windsor Castle, Maratta executed an *Annunciation* in 1659 for the high altar of the Church of S. Antonio Abbate at Anagni, and produced an engraving of the subject (ibid., fig. 4). Preparatory drawings for the paintings may be found at the Morgan Library, New York, and at the Kunstmuseum, Düsseldorf (ibid., figs. 8 and 5), where there is also a drawing for the engraving (ibid., fig. 3). Two others, at Holkham Hall, Leicester, England, were recently discussed by Clovis Whitfield and Gabriel Naughton (Holkham, 1977, nos. 75 and 76). Studio versions of Maratta's painting include one in the Hermitage, Leningrad, attributed to Niccolo Berettoni, a leading Maratta pupil (Stuffmann, 1968, p. 58); and paintings at the Palazzo Reale, Genoa; S. Pietro in Vincoli, Rome; and the Galleria Nazionale di Palazzo Corsini, Rome (Mezzetti, 1955, pp. 350–352). A studio sketch after the engraving is located at Windsor Castle (Blunt and Cooke, 1960, no. 306). Another composition sketch, apparently by the same hand, is in the Academia de Bellas Artes de San Fernando, Madrid.   A.A.

22

23

Pier Francesco Mola
Colderio (Como) 1612 – Rome 1668

23   Caricature of a Man with a Musket, Riding a Donkey in a Pond

194 x 204. Pen and brown ink; cream paper; repaired losses due to corrosion of paper from ink, erased by a later hand lower r., backed with antique laid paper. INSCR, brown ink, verso, in Uvedale Price's hand: *Mola. N. Price bought of Gialdoni at Rome, 1768*; black ink: 967; graphite: 5. PROV: Gialdoni; Uvedale Price (L. 2048); Sir J. C. Robinson; John Malcolm; The Hon. A. E. Gathorne-Hardy; Geoffrey Gathorne-Hardy; The Hon. Robert Gathorne-Hardy, Sotheby's, April 28, 1976, no. 27 (ill.). BIBL: Robinson, 1869, no. 265; Gathorne-Hardy, 1902, no. 22; Colnaghi, 1971, no. 56; Metropolitan Museum, 1976

For many artists in the seventeenth century, caricature was a witty and playful sideline practiced for strictly private amusement. Inspired by the grotesques of Michelangelo and Leonardo, caricature was developed into a distinct genre in Italy by the Bolognese artists Agostino and Annibale Carracci, and was soon practiced by Guercino, Bernini, Domenichino, and Pier Francesco Mola.

Among Mola's caricatures are at least two series with narrative overtones. One, which includes a drawing in the Scholz Collection and several examples in Berlin, depicts the exploits of a masked, clown-like figure. The other series centers upon the unshaven character in the Steiner drawing, with his hooked nose, mustache, and head of pale, puffy hair. Here our hero is nonplussed because the cannon fired from the tower in the background scares away the ducks he had intended to shoot.

Like the Steiner sheet, most of the drawings of the second series have a scatological element. Janos Scholz notes that this group of caricatures bears a resemblance in theme and style to several drawings by Guercino in his collection; moreover, because their style is distinct from other caricatures by Mola which reveal the influence of Bernini, they probably date from Mola's presumed stay in Bologna during the 1640s (Sutherland Harris, 1964, pp. 363–368). The narrative behind these scenes may also have a Bolognese source.

Janos Scholz has kindly provided a list of the known drawings from the second series: (1) *Man Carving a Capon* and (2) *Composition of Eight Figures* (Ashmolean Museum, Oxford; Parker, 1956, nos. 914 and 915); (3) *Vanitas*, (4) *Hanging the Donkey*, and (5) *Cleric Dictating His Last Will* (all in the collection of Janos Scholz; the latter two contain the same donkey found in the Steiner drawing; [5] ill. in RISD, 1971, p. 68); (6) *A Christening* (formerly in the collection of A. P. Oppé); (7) *Astronomer Introduced by Truth to Archimedes* (Worcester Art Museum; Vey, 1958, p. 67).   A.A.

24   Immaculate Conception

348 x 272. Pen and brown and grey ink and wash, black chalk underdrawing, incised with stylus; cream paper; restored loss lower center. INSCR, grey ink, lower left: *Pietro da Cortona*; on backing paper, in 18th-century hand: *Pietre Beretini da Cortonna / No 19 du cabinet D. Huquiere.* PROV: D. Huquier (L. 1285); Lowe, 1976, no. 19 (ill.)

Mola draws with a fluid, somewhat nervous line and broad areas of unmodulated wash, freely applied. His style bears a resemblance to Roman artists such as Pietro da Cortona, whose strong influence on Mola is attested to by this drawing's old attribution to that master. Mola, however, softened the monumentality of Roman painting with the sensuous light typical of the styles of Venice and Bologna, where he had spent much time prior to 1647 (Sutherland Harris, 1964, pp. 363–368).

Ann Sutherland Harris has orally dated this drawing to the 1650s on stylistic grounds. Its composition is closest to a drawing of the *Trinity with Adoring Angels* in Edinburgh, dated to before 1662 (Rowlands, 1964, p. 274). Finished pen and wash drawings are rare in Mola's published oeuvre; closest to the Steiner sheet is the *Adoration of the Shepherds* in the Louvre (Cocke, 1972, fig. 14), datable after Mola's return to Rome in 1641. However, forms in the *Immaculate Conception* are much more clearly defined and draperies are more airy and articulated. The drawing thus approaches in style Mola's Roman masterpiece *Joseph Greeting His Brethren* of 1656–1657, in the Quirinal. The distinctive broad facial type of the Virgin also appears

24

most frequently during these years, as in two paintings dated 1652–1657, *The Expulsion of Hagar* and *Bacchus* (ibid., ills. 91 and 92).

Mola's only representation of the Immaculate Conception mentioned in the archival sources was a church standard, now lost, painted for Prince Camillo Pamphili around 1656–1657 (ibid., pp. 4, 56, 72; Cocke calls it an *Assumption*). The standard is described in old accounts both as an *Immaculate Conception* and as an *Assumption*, a common confusion due to the similar iconography of these two subjects. Depictions of the Immaculate Conception, which derive their attributes from the text of Revelation 12:1, show the Virgin with her head crowned by twelve stars and her feet resting on a crescent moon. To distinguish the image from an Assumption, the Virgin's glance is usually focused downward.

If the Steiner drawing is indeed for the Pamphili standard, it is the first visual record of the project to be identified.   A.A.

Jacopo Palma the Younger, called *Palma Giovane*
Venice 1544–1628

25   Saint Onophrius in the Wilderness

210 x 145. Irongall ink and sepia wash over black chalk underdrawing; off-white paper; watermark: crossbow within a circle, with illegible monogram, similar to Briquet nos. 763, 767, 769. PROV: Giuseppe Vallardi (L. 1223); Julius Boehler

The grandnephew of Palma Vecchio, Palma Giovane was a prolific painter and draughtsman, and is known to have finished Titian's *Pietà* after the master's death (Freedberg, 1971, p. 352). Freedberg characterizes Palma's art as an eclectic assimilation of the various mannerist influences dominant in Venice during the 1570s (ibid., pp. 384–385). The light, nervous line and strong facial accents in this drawing, as well as the cursory indication of shadows and textures with rough scribbles, are characteristic of such Palma drawings as *Saint Jerome* and the *Study of an Old Man*, both in the Accademia di San Luca in Rome (Grassi, 1968, figs. 4 and 39). Despite its free application, however, the line does not indicate definite contours and

25

outlines; similarities to such drawings as the *Study for an Angel*, also in the Accademia di San Luca (ibid., fig. 30), suggest that this drawing dates from 1605–1610.

Hermit saints in the wilderness were popular subjects in the Renaissance, especially Saint Jerome. Scenes depicting Saint Jerome usually include his attributes of a lion or cardinal's hat. The palm trees and rocks surrounding the figure, as well as his long hair and rosary, all suggest that it is rather Saint Onophrius who is shown here. Onophrius, a hermit in the Egyptian desert, was known as the "hairy anchorite" (Réau, 1958, III, 720–721). The figure is similar in both appearance and orientation to *Saint Onophrius Penitent*, an engraving by Cornelis Cort after Girolamo Muziano (Bierens de Haan, 1948, no. 119, fig. 34). T.S.

Francesco Maria Mazzola, called *Parmigianino*
Parma 1503 – Casalmaggiore 1540

26 Minerva Drawing Her Sword from Its Scabbard
200 x 108. Pen and black ink over indications with a stylus; off-white paper. PROV: Sir Peter Lely (L. 2092); Sir Joshua Reynolds (L. 2364); Christie's, Dec. 9, 1975, no. 15 (frontispiece)

This elegant drawing displays the staccato penwork of Parmigianino's late phase in Parma, 1531–1540. Typical of the artist's mature *maniera* style, the *Minerva* synthesizes Roman sculptured form and the delicate modeling with light typical of the Parmesan school of the period.

A red chalk drawing in the Louvre shows the same figure in reverse. Popham identifies the Louvre *Minerva* as a seventeenth-century copy after a lost original, tentatively assigned to Parmigianino's late period (see Popham, 1971, pl. 394). The Steiner drawing may also relate to a smaller sketch in Parma (ibid., no. 558, pl. 394), which portrays a similar subject but lacks the robust quality of the Steiner *Minerva*. The pelvis of the Parma figure surges out and the sword is held in a more vertical position, accentuating the static

and ornamental posture. Even in its more sketchy state, the Parma drawing suggests that the artist intended a flaccid form.

An allegorical figure in the right hand corner of Parmigianino's *Portrait of Count San Secondo* in the Prado, Madrid, datable to 1533–1535 (Freedberg, 1951, pp. 212–213, figs. 139 and 140), is executed with the same concentration on decorative form that marks the Parma sketch. Since Parmigianino was known to have reworked his concepts many times before settling upon a final design, the Steiner drawing may represent an earlier, more dynamic plan for the accompanying figure in the Madrid portrait. In fact, the artist shifted the position of the figure on this sheet: a first outline is faintly visible to the left of the figure drawn in pen. A stylus underdrawing can be found in studies for other works by Parmigianino of this period, such as the *Madonna del Collo Lungo* (ca. 1535)—confirming a date contemporaneous with the San Secondo portrait.   A.K.

Giulio Pippi, called Giulio Romano
Rome 1499 – Mantua 1546

27   Putto on a Crouching Horse

122 x 162. Pen and brown ink; white paper. INSCR, pen and brown ink, in a 16th- or 17th-century hand, lower r.: *Giulio Romano*. PROV: King Charles I (?); Nicholas Lanier (L. 2886); Pierre-Jean Mariette (L. 1852); Count Moriz von Fries (L. 2903); Sir Thomas Lawrence (L. 2445); Lord Francis Egerton, first earl of Ellesmere (L. Suppl. 2710b), Sotheby's, Dec. 5, 1972, part II, no. 23. BIBL: Ellesmere, 1898, no. 177; Hartt, 1958, I, 126 and 296, no. 159

Giulio Romano was the major pupil of Raphael and the only Italian artist mentioned by Shakespeare. Most of his work was done in Mantua, where he settled after 1524 as a court painter to the Gonzaga. This drawing belongs to the corpus of work done in the 1520s for the Palazzo del Te, and it was Frederick Hartt who first recognized the sheet as a preliminary study for one of the smaller stucco medallions that surround four large fresco panels on the ceiling of the Sala delle Aquile (Hartt, 1958, I, 126). Although this medallion is not a central element in the overall decoration, it reflects and unites several themes of the ceiling: the putto mirrors other putti represented on

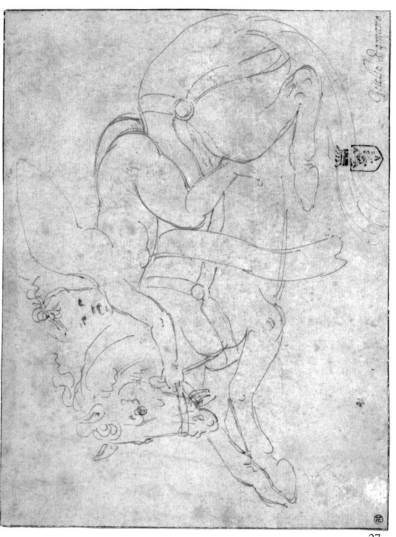

28

the vault, but through its isolation in a medallion it emphasizes the theme of love; the tense, crouching horse, full of unreleased energy, evokes the amorous abductions depicted elsewhere (for the complete iconography of the room see ibid., pp. 123–126).

Like *Two Putti on the Back of an Elephant*, a similar medallion study also in the Ellesmere sale, the Steiner drawing is made up of light flowing lines that move quickly through the sheet. As one of the first renderings of the design, it contains all the vitality that would later be lost in the drier, more exact drawing which the actual stucco medallion would be made from. Though lacking the wash that Giulio often used, the sheet has both a quiet delicacy and great potential energy, and complements the two moods that dominate the space for which the drawing was intended: love and violence.

P.F.

Salvator Rosa
Naples 1615–1673

28 Sheet of Studies

272 x 198. Pen and brown ink with grey wash; white paper; upper edge cut and tinted red, watermark: paschal lamb with pennant in circle. PROV: Queen Christina of Sweden (?); Decio, Cardinal Azzolini; Marchesa Pompeo Azzolini; Prince Livio Odescalchi; Ladislao Odescalchi; Christie's, March 30, 1976, pl. 14 (ill.). BIBL: Mahoney, 1977, pp. 407–408, no. 40.12

Rosa's aggressive individuality and his fascination with the morbid and mystical made him a forerunner of the Romantic movement. He claimed that he never had a master; Kitson (1973, p. 8) notes that although Rosa's taste for dark and morbid scenes is characteristic of Seicento painting in Naples and his interest in the picturesque comes from Florence, his style is neither Neapolitan nor Florentine. In spite of Rosa's statements to the contrary, the art of his early teacher Aniello Falcone did influence him, at least in his choice of subject matter. From Falcone Rosa learned to paint "battle scenes without a hero" (Saxl, 1939–1940, p. 70), the subject of the Steiner sketches and a theme which he repeated in numerous works. For political and intellectual reasons this subject was quite fashionable during the period 1630 to 1660 but, as Salerno points out (1963, pp. 46–47), while Falcone and other popular artists treated it as a genre theme, Rosa painted "ideal battles" which had a new heroic character and were infused with the violence of his personality. The fiery passion of these paintings is also evident in the drawings.

Mahoney (1977, pp. 407–408) has connected the Steiner sheet with the Louvre *Battaglia Eroica* which was painted in Rome for M. Corsini in 1652 as an intended gift for Louis XIV. The head at the lower left of the drawing is comparable to that of a horseman wearing a pelt at the right of the painting. A similar head is found on a sheet now in Leipzig (Schmidt, 1932, pl. 53) which contains other sketches for the Louvre painting. An even closer correspondence exists between the figures of the crouching soldier stabbing a fallen victim and the *Grande Battaglia di Cavalleria* in Auckland (Salerno, 1970, pl. 45).

Since this drawing and those at Leipzig were probably once part of the same collection (Mahoney, 1977, p. 407) it is likely that they furnished the inspiration for several of the battle pieces. Rosa signed most of the drawings which he sold or gave away, and the fact that all these sketches are unsigned indicates that he probably kept them in his studio. The Steiner sheet may have been among those to which Rosa referred when he wrote to his friend and patron Ricciardi in 1652, "I do not send you the sketches of the [Louvre] battlepiece, as it is necessary that I should keep them myself, to avoid repetitions on a further occasion" (Morgan, 1824, p. 262).

In the 1650s, Rosa stopped painting battle scenes, which he considered undignified, in an effort to achieve recognition as a history painter. He wrote to Ricciardi in 1652, "I have almost made a vow not to paint any more such pictures unless they are paid for at the rate of a Titian or a Raphael!" (ibid., p. 258).   R.Z.

Giovanni Battista della Rovere
Milan ca. 1551 – after 1627

29   Scene from the Life of San Carlo Borromeo

231 x 338. Black chalk, pen and brown ink, grey and brown wash, heightened with white; blue paper. PROV: Christie's, June 25, 1974, no. 35

This drawing was originally titled *Prelate Receiving a Deputation of Priests*. The central kneeling figure, however, bears a strong resemblance to the portrait type associated with Carlo Borromeo, the Milanese cardinal whose canonization in 1610 produced a wave of visual propaganda in the first two decades of the seventeenth century. Of three known picture cycles, one in the reception room of the Collegio Borromeo in Pavia and two in the Milan Cathedral, this drawing most closely resembles the *quadroni* in the Milan Cathedral. The first Milan series dealt with Borromeo's life and the second with his miracles. His supplicating gesture in the Steiner drawing links this work with the cycle depicting his life, dated 1602–1604.

Five paintings in this series are attributed to Giovanni Battista della Rovere, who was one of seven artists commissioned for the twenty works. In spite of the artist's use of the conventional format adopted for the *quadroni*, this drawing is not a study for the eventual contributions of Giovanni Battista or his brother Giovanni Mauro della Rovere, with whom he is often confused. Nancy Ward Nielson (1969, p. 239) suggests that each of the artists submitted drawings for all or many scenes, and that the paintings were subsequently divided between them. The finished state of this drawing, in comparison with hasty sketches in the Accademia Carrara in Bergamo (Bergamo, 1962, pls. 43, 44) for *San Carlo Carrying the Sacred Nail in a Procession*, an oil actually executed for the life cycle, may indicate that this scene was rejected from the final lot.

The brittle *maniera* figures, architectural delineation, and use of dark wash to mask a two-dimensional surface treatment distinguish the hand of Giovanni Battista from the more fluid hand of his brother.   A.K.

Agostino Buonamici, called *Tassi*
Perugia ca. 1582 – Rome 1664

30   Diana the Huntress with Her Hounds

229 x 165. Pen and brown ink and brown wash; white paper; laid down. INSCR, graphite, on backing: *Domenchino*. PROV: Lowe, 1976, no. 30

30

Despite Agostino Tassi's prominent position as teacher of Claude Lorrain, and as a collaborator with Cantagallina, Domenichino, Guercino, and others, we know relatively little about him. From his own statements and those of the biographer Passeri, we know that Tassi went to sea from the port of Livorno around 1595 and apparently spent the next decade or more working on galley-ships, possibly in involuntary servitude (Hess, 1935, p. 9). Whatever the circumstances, his maritime experiences made a lasting impression which resulted in his use of ships, ports, fishermen, storms, and shipwrecks in ornamental landscapes. He is known for the decoration of several palaces where his scenes are part of painted illusionistic architectural settings.

The attribution of this drawing to Tassi is firmly supported by Marco Chiarini (letter to Lorna Lowe, September, 1976), who has also compared it to *Erminia among the Shepherds*, dated to the third decade of the seventeenth century, in the Uffizi (Chiarini, 1972, pl. 27). A drawing even closer to the *Diana* (also from the same decade) is *Ariadne Abandoned*, in the Santarelli Collection, Florence (Hess, 1935, pl. xxiib). All three drawings share a similar treatment of trees and foliage, and an elegance of figure and animal representation. The *Diana* and the *Ariadne* are notably similar in composition, with the grove of trees behind the figure, the sloping ground line, and the tree or ship in the distance. During this same period, around 1624–1630, Tassi worked on the decoration of the Palazzo Doria-Pamphili (Hess, 1935, p. 23, pls. xxiii–xxvii), where similar compositional arrangements of ships, trees, and figures are repeated in a frieze-like series.   N.H.

Tiziano Vecellio, called *Titian*
Pieve di Cadore ca. 1490 – Venice 1576

31   Trees near Some Water

243 x 207. Brown ink and wash over black charcoal; white paper.
PROV: Yvonne Tan-Bunzl. BIBL: Oberhuber, 1976, no. 36 bis

31

Of the very few sheets preserved from Titian's large drawn oeuvre, many are studies of trees and landscapes related to his woodcuts. It is possible that these were treasured by early collectors and thus escaped the fate of most of his working drawings, which seem to have disappeared soon after his death. The Steiner sheet remained unrecognized until Julien Stock raised the question of whether it could not be by the same hand as the famous *Edge of a Wood* in the Metropolitan Museum (Oberhuber, 1976, no. 23), universally recognized as a work by the great Venetian. Indeed, the Steiner sheet shows a similar sense for the rich grandeur of vegetation, yet here the artist is no longer interested in the voluminous mass of the tree trunks, nor in uniting the leaves into large masses according to formulae derived from the woodcuts of Albrecht Dürer. Instead, he seeks to describe the nature of the foliage of each type of tree found in the dense vegetation lining the water. His interest is in the flecks and patterns with which the leaves reflect the sunlight falling on them in rich abundance, creating dense and mysterious shadows beneath.

In individual details and in the handling of the pen, the sheet is closest to drawings by Titian like the one in Edinburgh (ibid., no. 37), especially in the latter's best-preserved part in the upper left corner, where Titian deals with a similar problem of rendering dense bushes. The little figures in charcoal, just visible at the lower right corner of our sheet, are similar to slight sketches on the verso of the Edinburgh drawing, published by Bert Meijer (1974, p. 83, fig. 105). The trunks, on the other hand, are handled almost exactly like the branch in the upper part of the *Tree and Castle*, formerly in a Paris private collection (Oberhuber, 1976, fig. 11). Both of these drawings were used in Titian's woodcut *Saint Jerome in the Wilderness* (Rosand and Muraro, 1976–1977, no. 22), datable on stylistic grounds to around 1530. There is also a great similarity between the handling of foliage in the Steiner sheet and in the woodcut *Stigmatization of Saint Francis* (ibid., no. 24) of about the same date. Much later, in the *Landscape with a Horse and a River* (ibid., no. 47), Titian again characterizes the water in a way similar to the Steiner sheet. The drawing is unusually well preserved and therefore shows Titian's stroke in its richest splendor. K.O.

Giovanni dei Ricamatori, called Giovanni da Udine

Udine 1487 – Rome 1564

32 Sketchbook Sheet of Ornamental Studies

320 x 225. Pen and brown ink; white paper; on verso, several figures traced through the back by a different hand; staining on both sides from adjacent pages. INSCR, pen, in 17th-century hand, upper l.: *Ego Francesco Lar.* PROV: Ferruccio Asta (L. Suppl. 116a); Chiltern Art Gallery

Giovanni da Udine, one of the leading decorators of the first half of the sixteenth century, is celebrated for his imitation of the antique ornamental style known as the grotesque, for the revival of classical stucco decoration, and for his lifelike representation of animals and plants. The only drawings that can be reliably attributed to him are watercolors and gouaches like the ones in the British Museum, Dresden, and Vienna (Pouncey and Gere, 1962, no. 153; Oberhuber, 1972, nos. 473a and b), all nature studies related to work in the Vatican Loggia. However, since none of the pen drawings attributed to Giovanni are certain (see Pouncey and Gere, 1962, p. 109), his style in this medium is still an enigma.

General aspects of this sheet closely parallel Giovanni's decorative work, and may support an attribution to him. Giovanni da Udine went from his native Veneto to Rome, where he became Raphael's assistant. This drawing is stylistically similar to an ornamental drawing of Venetian origin in the Fogg Collection (Mongan and Sachs, 1940, fig. 41); both handle light and line in a characteristic Northern Italian manner. But at the same time, this sheet has a heightened sense of classical form and proportion, relating it to the style of the Raphael school.

In the decoration of the Loggia, work with very similar style, motifs, and composition can be seen in both the fresco decoration of the pilasters and in the carved wooden doors (Cecchelli, 1928, pp. 315–317). Certain putti, swans, and foliage are extremely close to elements in this sheet. Yet these frieze studies relate better to the classical and compact decorative style found in Giovanni's stucco work, especially in the Villa Madama in Rome. They have less in

32

common with his light, open, and fantastic wall decorations in the grotesque style, where the figures appear in greater movement and are more tightly modeled in the round. This drawing with its highly controlled outlines and parallel shading retains so much of the Quattrocento tradition of Northern Italy that if the attribution to Giovanni is correct, it would have to be a work done very early in his Roman years.   P.F.

Pietro Buonaccorsi, called Perino del Vaga
Florence 1500 – Rome 1547

33   Saint Peter

215 x 315. Pen and brown ink, squared in black chalk; off-white paper; irongall corrosion, ink blotches, watermark: encircled, unidentified. PROV: Yvonne Tan-Bunzl, 1975, no. 25 (ill.)

Primarily a draughtsman and a decorator in fresco and tapestry, Perino del Vaga began his career in Florence and Rome. A principal student of Raphael, he was also influenced by Rosso, Parmigianino, and Michelangelo. Perino worked in Rome except for the period 1528–1536, when he went to Genoa and Pisa. Of his many drawing studies, most are in pen, a technique well suited to his fluid and cursive line.

This sketch of *Saint Peter*, unusual because Perino seldom chose a single figure as his subject, relates to two other studies of the saint, probably for an unknown fresco. They all place Saint Peter in a triangular frame, perhaps the spandrel of a vault.

One of these study sheets, in an English private collection (Edinburgh, 1969, no. 59, pl. 62), appears to be a quick preparatory sketch for the third and most finished one, in the Albertina (Davidson, 1966, no. 25, pl. 20). Davidson relates the Albertina drawing to Perino's altar in Celle Ligure and to his *Saint Erasmus* altarpiece in Genoa. She tentatively dates it to Perino's second period in Genoa after his return from Pisa (around 1535–1536).

Yet when compared to another of Perino's drawings, his *Nativity with Saints* (ibid., no. 24, pl. 24), datable to 1534, the Albertina sheet

seems to be from the same period: an angular faceting of light, similar head types, and elegant, elongated figures characterize both drawings.

The Steiner sheet is clearly earlier than the two other studies of Saint Peter. It shows Perino at the beginning of his Genoese career (1529–1530), continuing in his earlier Roman style influenced by Michelangelo. The rounded, heavily draped figure resembles those in Perino's decoration of the Cappella del Crocifisso, S. Marcello al Corso, Rome (Oberhuber, 1966, p. 177), which reveal his indebtedness to Michelangelo's Sistine Chapel. It resembles also the figures in Perino's early frescoes in the Sala de' Trionfi, Palazzo Doria, Genoa, particularly in the *Triumph of the Roman Consul, Aemilius Paulus*, and *Gods and Goddesses* (Askew, 1966, pp. 48, 52, pls. 22, 23, 25–27, 29).

The Steiner drawing thus leads us to assume that Perino received the commission for a fresco with Saint Peter early in his Genoese period.   L.K.

34   Studies of Horses

286 x 389. Pen and brown ink; white paper; mounted in full on secondary sheet with "gold" painted border. INSCR, pen, verso (now covered by mounting paper): *Perino del Vaga 18 56*. PROV: Nicholas Lanier (L. 2885); Sir Peter Lely (L. 2092); William Mayor (L. 2799); Lord Roseberry; Sotheby's, Nov. 21, 1974, no. 16 (ill.)

Because powerfully moving horses in fierce combat were first introduced into Renaissance art by Leonardo da Vinci, this impressive drawing was once attributed to him. Yet as John Gere and Jacob Bean first recognized, the old attribution to Perino del Vaga on the back of the sheet, now covered by the backing paper, is clearly correct. Compared to Leonardo's great steeds in the *Battle of Anghiari*, which obviously gave the artist his inspiration for this work, Perino's horses are lighter and more agile. They demonstrate his concern with the observation of anatomy, with foreshortening, and with movement. Similar muscular action, clear structure, forceful outlining, and shading with long, parallel strokes can be found in Perino's *Two Duelling Warriors* (Davidson, 1966, no. 21, fig. 23), dated by Davidson to Perino's first Genoese period, in the early

thirties. It is likely that this unusually grand study sheet dates from the same time, when Perino was occupied with heroic subjects in his frescoes for the Palazzo Doria.   L.K. and K.O.

Giorgio Vasari
Arezzo 1511 – Florence 1573

35   The Incredulity of Saint Thomas

218 x 186. Black chalk, pen and brown ink, brown wash, squared in black chalk; white paper. INSCR, pen, in cartouches: *Beati qui no viderut; et crediderunt*; chalk, on mount: *Giorgio Vasari*. PROV: Christie's, March 30, 1976, no. 1 (ill.)

Better known as the author of *Lives of the Artists*, Vasari was a prolific painter of the High *Maniera*. This work is characteristic of his drawing style: extreme facility of penmanship, echoed in the febrile fluency of the inscriptions and the almost rococo touch of the ornamental border, and heightened with loosely applied wash, the whole possessing a certain grace and surface drama. As the artist wrote,

He who has not drawn much, nor studied selected antique or modern things, cannot work well from memory by himself; nor can he improve the things that are depicted from life by giving them that grace and perfection which art gives beyond the order of nature, since the latter ordinarily does some parts that are not beautiful. (Vasari-Milanesi, 1880, VII, 447; tr. in Poirier, 1970, p. 62)

In about 1556, returning to a theme that was a favorite of the Counter-Reformation and his old master Francesco Salviati, he produced the *Incredulity of Saint Thomas* for the Guidacci Chapel in Santa Croce. The Steiner drawing is an earlier design for an altarpiece, probably contemporary with the *Saints Peter and John Blessing* of 1557 in the Staatliche Museum, Berlin (Barocchi, *Pittori*, 1964, pl. 71), which shares the packed surface, the sense of atmospheric volume, and the expressiveness of the onlookers' faces. Vasari's interpretation of the subject is unusual in its juxtaposition of Doubting Thomas with Saint Peter, the believer, who appears behind the figure of Christ. Vasari thus creates a complex conflict of rhythm. The faces are striking in their calligraphic delineation.   C.R.S.-S.

35

Attributed to Giorgio Vasari

36 Two Figures, half length

290 x 285. Red chalk; white heavy North Italian paper; tear from upper edge into r. figure (retouched), watermark: paschal lamb in circle with monogram *AB* (similar to Briquet, I, 21, no. 53); INSCR, graphite, verso, top r.: *D.84*; grey ink, lower r. corner: *no.2.* PROV: Lili Frohlich-Bume; Yvonne Tan-Bunzl; William H. Schab Gallery (Catalogue, 1970, no. 3 [ill. cover])

This drawing is of very high quality: with contrasted movement and emphatic lighting, it dramatically illustrates the dialogue between two figures, perhaps apostles, one far-seeing and idealistic, the other inquiring. Yet it presents grave problems of attribution. First given to Vasari by the William Schab Gallery, the attribution was accepted, with reservations, by Philip Pouncey. It has something of Vasari's late, more rounded style (as seen, for example, in the *Incredulity of Saint Thomas* in Santa Croce); the costume and watermark would also date it late in his career. Yet Vasari's only other known drawing of this type—chalk with vigorous outlines—is much earlier and very different in its clipped and severe character (Uffizi inv. 6494 F; Barocchi, *Disegni*, 1964, no. 10, fig. 3). Thus there is no way of accepting it with certainty as part of the oeuvre of the admittedly eclectic artist. Its rhetoric might even suggest a later date and its soft light may indicate influence from outside Florence.   C.R.S.-S.

Baldassare Franceschini, called Il Volterrano
Volterra 1611 – Florence 1689

37 Three Projects for a *Theatrum Sacrum*

265 x 400. Red chalk; cream paper; red chalk stain lower r. edge, darkened glue stains at all edges, insect damage upper edge, r., and lower edge, watermark: bridled horse surmounted by a cross. INSCR, graphite, lower l.: *SS* [55?]. PROV: H. M. Calmann, Christie's, March 26, 1974, no. 45, pl. 17

Baldassare Franceschini, called Il Volterrano, was a leading fresco painter in Florence during the second half of the seventeenth century. First trained as a sculptor by his father, Gasparo, he then studied

36

in Florence under Matteo Rosselli and later assisted Giovanni da San Giovanni in the decoration of the Sala degli Argenti in the Pitti Palace. His most famous work, the decoration of SS. Annunziata in Florence, reveals the influence of Correggio and Pietro da Cortona.

These three sketches are for a reliquary tomb set into a niche decorated with the assumption of a saint in its vault. They were made as preliminary designs for the decorations erected in honor of the canonization of the Carmelite nun Santa Maria Maddalena de' Pazzi, which took place in Florence in 1669. The final appearance of the *theatrum sacrum* designed by Volterrano is recorded in a print by Theodor Verkruys (Adimari, 1706, ill. facing p. 83) and corresponds except for minor details to the final sketch at the far right.

A drawing by Volterrano in the Albertina (Stix, 1932, no. 691, pl. 156) of a similar sarcophagus supported by caryatids has been identified by Lankheit as a study for the same decoration (Lankheit, 1962, p. 43). A drawing in the Metropolitan Museum of Art showing the same sarcophagus inside an elaborate catafalque decorated with candles (Metropolitan Museum, 1976, no. 17) is probably for the same project.

The Steiner and Metropolitan drawings as well as a third study, all sold at Christie's in 1974, were part of a larger group of Volterrano drawings in the possession of H. M. Calmann that is now dispersed.   s.c.

Workshop of Taddeo Zuccaro
Sant'Angelo 1529 – Rome 1566

38   Sea Battle in the Gulf of Morbihan

305 x 432. Black chalk underdrawing, with red wash and white gouache; cream paper; watermark: Briquet 3395. PROV: Baron von Kühlen (?) (unlisted collector's stamp in lilac: *Kühlen* [in oval]; 64); Pietro Scarpa

The two brothers Taddeo and Federico Zuccaro were the leading artists of Rome in the second half of the sixteenth century, yet they never lost contact with the *Marche*, the region where they, and Raphael, were born. In 1560 Taddeo returned to Urbino to paint the Duke's daughter, and there received the commission for a set of

designs to be used by the Fontana family's celebrated majolica factory of Urbino in producing a service to be sent as a gift to the King of Spain. This service, illustrating the life of Julius Caesar, was complete by December, 1562 (Gere, 1963, p. 306). Most of the pieces in the set are now lost, but John Gere (ibid., and 1969, pp. 89–93) has succeeded in identifying some of its parts and reconstructing others with the help of majolica copies and preparatory drawings by Taddeo and his workshop.

There is reason to believe that the Steiner sheet represents a design for a lost cistern in the "Spanish Service." A. E. Popham, describing a drawing in Windsor Castle (Popham and Wilde, 1949, no. 987) that faithfully copies the same composition, observed that it was a counterpart to another *Naval Battle* in the British Museum, a copy from a lost design by Taddeo (Gere, 1963, p. 309, fig. 22; 1969, no. 100). The cistern related to the British Museum composition still exists in the Museo Nazionale in Florence (Gere, 1963, fig. 16). Moreover, both *Battles* were readapted to oval cisterns now in the Wallace Collection (ill. *Apollo* XLII [1945]: 300) and in the Prado, the former signed F.F.F. (Flaminio Fontana Fecit) and dated 1574 (Gere, 1963, p. 313).

Yet Gere had doubts about the relationship of the Windsor—and by implication, the Steiner—*Naval Battles* to the "Spanish Service." Some of the drawings' essential elements appear in the background of one of Taddeo's frescoes in the Sala Regia in the Vatican, *The Siege of Tunis*, probably not begun before 1564, two years after the completion of the set (ill. Gere, 1963, fig. 32; 1969, pl. 159). Gere concluded that this composition was rather a pastiche made in Taddeo's shop, possibly after the artist's death in 1566.

Closer observation, however, speaks against this conclusion. The rounded forms of the antique ships, fantastically reconstructed by Taddeo from sculpted classical prototypes, fit beautifully into the round of the design. A very specific action is depicted. Soldiers in small rowboats have surrounded larger sailing vessels and are attempting to cut down their rigging with sickles attached to poles. All the basic elements of the composition are subordinated to this incident, the decisive fact in the defeat of the powerful fleet of the Veneti by the Romans under Julius Caesar in the Gulf of Morbihan in 56 B.C. In the fresco the same ships are simply lined up in the harbor of Tunis with no unifying narrative element. Surely, then, it is clear that the composition known from the Windsor and Steiner sheets was a design for the "Spanish Service" and thus precedes the fresco.

The red wash technique of the Steiner sheet corresponds to that of the one known finished drawing by Taddeo for this service (Louvre; Gere, 1969, no. 185, pl. 120), but the Steiner drawing differs from all others in that it includes indications for the decorative border, which incidentally differ from the ornament as executed. Also, the drawing style does not have quite the crispness expected from works in Taddeo's own hand. It must therefore be a working drawing produced by one of the major assistants in Taddeo's shop.

L.K. and K.O.

NORTHERN DRAWINGS

Abraham Bloemaert
Dordrecht 1564 – Utrecht 1651

39 The Prophet Elijah in the Desert, Fed by a Raven

124 x 98. Pen and light brown ink and wash, over black chalk, heightened with white now slightly darkened; white paper. PROV: H. van Leeuwen (L. Suppl. 2799a); Baron Bentinck; P. & D. Colnaghi, Kate de Rothschild

Abraham Bloemaert was an important transitional figure in the development of seventeenth-century Dutch art from Mannerism into the early Baroque style. Famous as an artist and teacher, during his long career his work partook of the stylistic developments of the first half of the seventeenth century. Among his students were his four sons and many of the important Caravaggist painters of the Utrecht school.

This drawing, clearly later than Bloemaert's work of his mannerist period, shows a greater understanding of the use of light to create natural forms. The artist skillfully employed the diffused, even light and shadows to model form and impart a feeling of openness. Graceful rendering of line in the cloak, and the greater sense of roundness in the figure, suggest an understanding of the new naturalism that was beginning to emerge in Dutch art in the third decade of the seventeenth century.

The style of this drawing, its size, and its religious subject matter are typical of Bloemaert drawings made as preparatory studies for engravings. As far as we know, this subject was not engraved by Bloemaert or his circle, and therefore cannot be dated exactly. However, comparison with a pastoral drawing in the Hermitage plausibly dated 1610–1612 (Koeznetsow and Tsesjkowskaja, 1972, fig. 8) clearly

39

shows our sheet to be a more mature work. The Hermitage drawing, an example of Bloemaert's late mannerist style, portrays exaggerated and posed human figures, with body features isolated by harsh patches of light and dark.

Two preparatory drawings by Bloemaert for his painting *Supper at Emmaeus*, 1622 (Kamenskaja, 1937, figs. 4, 5, 6), show a close stylistic affinity with the Steiner sheet in the use of soft, diffused light, and natural rendering of line to model the human form. A sheet of studies which Kamenskaja dates to 1629 (ibid., fig. 7) also makes use of the same soft, even light, and a natural rendering of the folds of clothing. Even though a satisfactory chronology of Bloemaert's oeuvre has not been established and his numerous drawings are difficult to date, comparison with drawings such as these suggests that this drawing may date from the 1620s.   R.M.

Ferdinand Bol
Dordrecht 1616 – Amsterdam 1680

40   The Raising of the Daughter of Jairus (?)

302 x 209. Pen and brush and brown ink and wash over graphite; buff paper; cracks throughout, mended on verso, tips of four corners replaced. PROV: Christie's, July 2, 1954, no. 291 (as *The Raising of Jairus' Daughter* by Rembrandt); Fischer, Lucerne, Dec. 1, 1956 (ill., as *Healing of the Sick*, School of Rembrandt); Galerie am Neumarkt, Zürich, May 25, 1972, no. 172, pl. 1 (as *Raising of the Daughter of Jairus*, School of Rembrandt, probably Aert de Gelder); Gabor Kekkoe (*Meisterzeichnungen* I, pl. 23)

The style of this sheet clearly supports the attribution to Bol endorsed by Wolfgang Wegner in 1972 and Werner Sumowski in 1974. Characteristic of Bol's drawings which have been dated to the mid-1630s are the loose, flowing outlines, the fine diagonal lines denoting shadow, and the extensive wash varying in tone and texture. One of Rembrandt's most talented pupils, Bol probably entered his studio around 1633–1634 and may have remained there until just before 1642, the time of his first dated painting (Haverkamp-Begemann and Logan, 1969, p. 183).

Until about 1650 Bol's drawings often come deceptively close to his teacher's style of the latter half of the thirties and the early forties. For instance, in this sheet Bol emulates the dynamic line and brief sketches of the mid-thirties. However, the more decorative quality of Bol's stroke (particularly noticeable in the lower half of the body of the recumbent woman in the Steiner sheet) and the greater use of background wash distinguish his drawings from those of his teacher. Like another Rembrandt pupil, Govaert Flinck, Bol eventually adopted the pale tonality and elegant gestures associated with the modish style of painting exemplified by Bartholomew van der Helst.

The subject of this drawing is uncertain. Sumowski's suggestion in correspondence that the scene represented is the death of Lucretia deserves consideration. The woman in the foreground appears to be dead; the object held in the hand of the principal male figure could be the knife used by Lucretia to stab herself. Furthermore, the position of Bol's prostrate woman is identical to that of Lucretia in a painting of *The Death of Lucretia* attributed to a Rembrandt pupil, Jan Victors (Valentiner, 1925–1934, II, p. xxx). Rembrandt executed two drawings of *The Raising of the Daughter of Jairus* in the early 1630s (Benesch, 1973, nos. 61, 62); however, the composition of these works differs from this drawing. Also, Rembrandt distinguishes Christ through the motif of radiance whereas His identity is not clear in this sheet.

As Sumowski observed in earlier correspondence, the Steiner drawing was engraved in the same direction by A. Laurentz in 1756 with the title *Christ Taking Leave of His Mother*, by Rembrandt (Weigel 7513).   c.s.

Andries Both
Utrecht ca. 1611 – Venice ca. 1641

41   Artist Seated at His Easel

140 x 187. Pen and brown ink; cream paper; residues of old ink stains lower l. and center of easel support, adhesive stains at all edges, illegible watermark surmounted by a crescent. INSCR, brown ink,

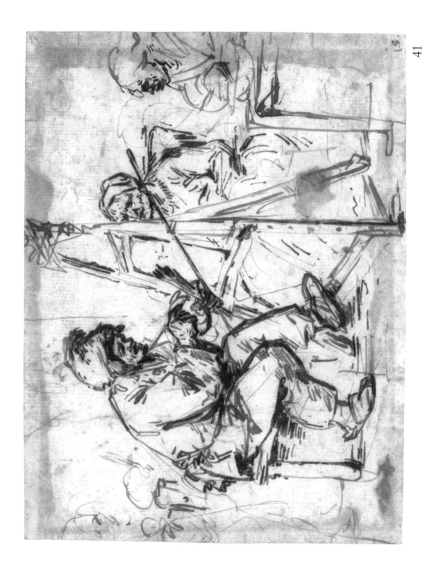

lower r.: *18*. PROV: Benjamin West; Sotheby's, Nov. 22, 1974, no. 112 (repr. actual size p. 97)

Verso: Fragmentary sketches for a dancing couple and a standing woman

Only recently has Andries Both, traditionally known only as the figure painter for his brother Jan's landscapes, gained recognition as a gifted artist in his own right (Waddingham, 1964). This drawing demonstrates Andries' spirited and candid treatment of lowlife scenes. These subjects occupied him all his life, but the Brouwerian gusto of the earlier works such as the Steiner sheet mellowed somewhat after the artist joined the circle of Pieter van Laer (Bamboccio) in Rome around 1635.

Artist Seated at His Easel probably dates from 1633–1635. During these years Andries traveled from Utrecht to Rome, stopping in Rouen in 1633. How long he stayed in France is not known, but his presence in Rome by 1635 is documented. Typical of Andries' touch in this period are the bold angular lines and the diagonal accents denoting shadow. In the splotchy dabs of ink describing the features of the figure on the right we detect Andries' bolder, blunter version of the abbreviated technique used by his teacher in Utrecht, Abraham Bloemart.

This drawing is related in subject and style to *The Artist in His Studio*, a painting signed and dated 1634, now in the Shapiro Collection in London. Compositions of the two works differ, however. In the painting, two ragged children and a woman grinding paints (possibly the occupation of the figure on the right in the sheet) stand behind the artist, whose direction is reversed from the drawing. The Shapiro Collection painting appears to fit into the pictorial tradition, common in seventeenth-century Holland, of allegorical representations of the impoverished artist which allude to the struggle for survival in times of war and strife. A sketch in the British Museum which has been attributed to Pieter de Bloot on the basis of a monogram *PDB* (Hind, 1915–1932, III, 43, no. 1) has the same composition as the painting. The relationship of this work to Both has never been investigated.

The studies on the verso resemble the slight sketch on the left edge of the sheet.   C.S.

Marten van Cleve (?)
Antwerp 1527–1581

42 Peasant Banquet

175 x 212. Pen and purplish ink; cream paper; slightly soiled at corners. INSCR, graphite: *Brueghel (Peter) 1530–1569*. PROV: Mathias Komor (L. Suppl. 1882a)

This peasant scene, possibly a wedding banquet, was at one time attributed to Frans Verbeeck of Mecheln (d. 1570). In spite of certain elements in common with his work—the elongated and angular figures with triangular faces, and the element of caricature—a Verbeeck attribution seems unlikely because of the quality of line, handling of space, and composition (see Berlin, 1975, nos. 269 and 270, pls. 155 and 157).

An attribution to Marten van Cleve was recently suggested (orally) by Emile Wolf. Indeed, the *Peasant Banquet* bears a closer kinship to the work of this artist than to that of Verbeeck, especially to the background passages of the *Peasant Kirmes* in Berlin (ibid., no. 134, pl. 153) and also to two drawings in the Albertina (Benesch, 1928, nos. 88 and 89). It can be related as well to a slightly larger drawing, sold at Sotheby's (April 9, 1970, no. 67 [ill.]), also drawn with pen and purplish-brown ink, which is similar both in theme and compositional structure.

The shared theme of peasant festivities, the depiction of small figures gesturing expressively, and the emphasis on outline link the Steiner drawing to these works. Van Cleve's line, however, is smooth and rounded, whereas the line in the Steiner sheet is busier, rougher, and more jagged. The scenes of revelry in the three drawings noted above are more restrained and rhythmically ordered than the more compact grouping of figures which creates the impression of boisterous activity in the Steiner sheet. Furthermore, here the aggressive diagonal of the table creates a spatial recession inconsistent with the handling of space in the accepted drawings by van Cleve.

Two factors may explain these differences: the first is the unusual sketchiness and lack of finish of the Steiner drawing, which may have been cut from a larger sheet. The second may have to do with van Cleve's development. Most of his known drawings seem to

42

belong to his later periods, when he was influenced by Pieter Brueghel and Gillis Mostaert, while the Steiner sheet is clearly closer to an early painting, *Flemish Housekeeping* in Vienna (Faggin, 1965, fig. 1). Painted under the influence of van Cleve's early mentors Frans Floris and Pieter Aertsen, *Flemish Housekeeping* is similar in the handling of composition and clustering of figures, and in the use of more elongated figure types with triangular faces. Yet even in this early painting, van Cleve's forms are more rounded and there is a greater circular movement to his line than in the Steiner drawing. Given the gaps in our knowledge, definite attribution of this free and charming drawing must await new evidence.   E.B.

Abraham van Diepenbeeck
Hertogenbosch (Bois-le-Duc) 1596 – Antwerp 1675

43   The Return of Jephtha
99 x 160. Pen and brown ink and brown wash heightened with white gouache over graphite; cream paper; laid down. INSCR, brown ink, upper r.: *10*; lower margin of secondary support: *23*; graphite, verso: *Sacrifice De Jephté / Diepenbeck.* PROV: Sotheby's, March 21, 1973, no. 18 (ill.)

Originally a glass-painter like his father and teacher Jan Roelofsz., Diepenbeeck turned to easel painting only around 1630. Although he made trips to Italy and England and probably to France, he was most strongly influenced by his own countryman Peter Paul Rubens, and may actually have been a member of the Rubens workshop (Wurzbach, 1906–1911, I, 403).

A prolific draughtsman, Diepenbeeck made many designs for prints and especially for book illustrations. The Steiner sheet is a fine example from the latter group. It is one of a series of drawings of Biblical stories of similar dimensions and techniques. The Louvre has four sheets, two illustrating the story of David and two showing scenes from the life of Christ (Lugt, 1949, nos. 554–558). *Lot and His Daughters*, which was sold in the same sale as the Steiner drawing in 1973 (no. 19), is now in a private collection in Cambridge, Massa-

chusetts; on December 13, 1973, a *Vision of Jacob's Ladder* was also sold at Sotheby's (no. 95). The British Museum owns one more, an *Adoration of the Magi* (Hind, 1915–1932, II, p. 102, no. 7). These compositions were probably intended to illustrate a new edition of the Bible, but the project must have been abandoned since no such Bible is known and none of the compositions were engraved (Hollstein, 1949–, V, 241–243).

The story of Jephtha is told in the eleventh chapter of the book of Judges. Before going to battle against the Ammonites, Jephtha swore to God that if he won he would sacrifice to Him the first person he would see upon his return home. As it happened, he was victorious, but to his horror it was his daughter and only child who greeted him. She insisted that he fulfill his promise, and was apparently sacrificed (Judg. 11:39). The Diepenbeeck illustration is quite literal, showing Jephtha tearing his clothes (11:35) at the sight of his daughter who comes to meet him "with timbrels and with dancing" (11:34). M.M.

Lambert Doomer
Amsterdam ca. 1624–1700

44 Rebecca and Eliezer at the Well

263 x 406. Pen and brown ink and colored washes; off-white paper. INSCR, brown ink, lower r.: *1696 Doomer.* PROV: J. den Bosch, sale, Amsterdam, Oct. 5, 1767, G-411; IJver; J. W. B. Wuyters, sale, Utrecht, Sept. 17, 1792, C-47; Chevalier Ignace-Joseph de Claussin, sale, Batignolles, Dec. 2, 1844, no. 27; Collection Defer-Dumesnil, sale, Paris, Hôtel Droûot, May 10, 1900, no. 66; K. T. Parker; Henry Oppenheimer; Francis Springell; Sotheby Mak van Waay, May 3, 1976, no. 234 (ill.). BIBL: Parker, 1929, p. 9 (ill.); Dattenberg, 1940, p. 16; Colnaghi, 1959, no. 48; *Illustrated London News*, Oct. 24, 1959; Edinburgh, 1965, no. 55; Schulz, *Doomer*, 1974, no. 42, fig. 19

The date on the drawing, as well as its style, place it at the end of Doomer's artistic career. Signed and dated drawings, common among Doomer's works, facilitate the documentation of his stylistic development (see Schulz, *Doomer*, 1974). His early style—broad, cursory, and spontaneous—was influenced considerably by Rembrandt, in

whose studio Doomer worked in 1644 and probably 1645. The drawing here, however, contains the nervous lines and miniaturesque detail common in his later works.

Doomer's drawings fall more or less into four categories: topographical landscapes (by far the largest group), genre scenes, animal studies, and Biblical subjects. While *Rebecca and Eliezer* comes into the last category, it incorporates aspects of Doomer's other types of drawings. For example, an earlier drawing (datable to around 1670) of the same subject (ibid., p. 36, fig. 11) differs compositionally from the Steiner drawing but contains a similar study of a camel and donkey against its left margin. Similarly, the foreground and middle ground here showing various extraneous groupings of figures is reminiscent of the artist's earlier genre scenes.

Instead of placing the Biblical theme in the accurate desert setting, Doomer chooses a rocky landscape background, characteristic of his late works. Specifically, the landscape is a *souvenir de voyage* taken from topographical drawings made on his Rhine journey begun in 1663. The cluster of towers on the right recalls the town of Bacharach in his earlier drawings (De Groot and Spies, 1926, figs. 4 and 5). Bacharach is here viewed from the north. The indistinct towers in the distance on the left may be those of Stahleck Castle (ibid., figs. 4 and 6), a building frequently included with scenes of Bacharach in Doomer's earlier drawings. The Steiner drawing is only one example of many in which Doomer resurrects his own previously used themes for use in his later works.   N.N.

Allaert van Everdingen
Alkmaar 1621 – Amsterdam 1675

45 River Landscape with Two Boats

102 x 150. Pen and brown ink and brown and grey wash over faint traces of black chalk; off-white paper. INSCR, pen and grey ink, on boat lower r.: *AVE*; on mount: *A VON EVERDINGEN*; chalk, verso: *no 35*; *Everdingen f2-10-*; graphite: *8-2 dessins*; *fu:z-*. PROV: N. D. Goldsmid (L. 1962); R. Burdon-Muller; Schaeffer Galleries. BIBL: Eisler, 1963, pl. 78 (incorrect title, technical description, and ownership)

Allaert van Everdingen, who is thought to have been a pupil of Roelant Savery and Pieter Molyn, is best known for his Scandinavian landscapes of foaming waterfalls and rocky mountain valleys. He also received considerable recognition as a marine painter. This drawing, with its fishing boats and flat terrain, falls into a third and less well known category of his drawings, Netherlandish scenes.

Everdingen's Netherlandish drawings, fewer in number and more varied in composition than his Scandinavian sheets, are only rarely dated and difficult to order chronologically. Scholars have dated them only as a group, placing them sequentially after his marine paintings, that is, after 1655 (see Davies, 1973, p. 237-2).

In contrast to Everdingen's earlier Scandinavian works, the Steiner drawing has simpler and more generalized forms, less tonal contrast, and smoother planar transitions. Moreover, because of the darkened foreground and diagonal recession, the eye is not led as directly into space as it is in the earlier works. Also, the subdued spirit of this drawing as well as its draughtsmanship liken it to several of Everdingen's Netherlandish sheets datable after the mid-fifties (see, for example, ibid., figs. 45, 338, 339). In fact, the circular building on the right of the Steiner drawing is repeated in another of his Netherlandish riverscapes (ibid., fig. 45).   N.N.

Govaert Flinck
Cleve 1615 – Amsterdam 1660

46   Portrait of a Man

260 x 206. Black and white chalk; blue paper. INSCR, brown ink, lower l.: *2-6 F.*; lower r.: *Wolfgangus Lu—*; verso: *Wolfgangus Ludowig de Salablanca*. PROV: Wolfgangus Ludowig de Salablanca (17th or 18th century); Charles Slatkin Galleries, 1973

This drawing is a preparatory study for *Portrait of a Man*, a painting signed by the artist and dated 1651 (van Moltke, 1965, no. 281). Flinck executed numerous drawings on colored paper in black chalk; however, finished portrait studies such as this sheet are relatively rare in his oeuvre. Some figure studies related to portraits of the late forties are known, but most of Flinck's chalk sketches on colored paper are drawings of nude women or figure studies not connected with finished works.

Through the interplay of soft, broad lines in the body, sharper accents on the face, and touches of white highlight, the artist evokes depth and volume in this study. The intense psychological penetration found in this drawing distinguishes it from the more academic and elegant style which is characteristic of Flinck's portraits from the fifties. The vivid characterization and the free, loose touch show that the lessons Flinck absorbed while he was a student in Rembrandt's studio (ca. 1633–1636) remained with him even after he drifted away from his teacher's style.

Flinck probably joined Rembrandt's studio together with another pupil, Jacob Backer, soon after they arrived in Amsterdam in 1632. Rembrandt did not pressure his students to imitate his style, but encouraged them to develop individual modes of expression (Haverkamp-Begemann and Logan, 1969, pp. 21–29). Flinck followed Rembrandt's style of the late thirties and early forties until around 1643, when he adopted the more fashionable mode of painting based upon van Dyck and Bartholomew van der Helst.

The early inscription in the lower right corner probably refers to a collector who has not been identified.   c.s.

Jacob de Gheyn II
Antwerp 1565 – The Hague 1629

47   Reclining Peasant

91 x 117. Pen and brown ink; grey-brown paper; about 10 mm. made up along upper edge, repair on lower l. corner. INSCR, black chalk, lower r.: *Gheyn (Jacob)*. PROV: Collection Prince Charles de Ligne, sale Nov. 4, 1794, p. 250, no. 1; J de la Gardie; Dr. E. Perman, Sotheby Mak van Waay, June 9, 1975, no. 37. BIBL: Stockholm, 1953, no. 74

Verso: Study of a Young Man

De Gheyn, an important Dutch Mannerist and brilliant draughtsman, was also active as an engraver and painter. By 1585 his serious

46

47

interest in engraving had led him to study for two years with Hendrik Goltzius, Haarlem's leading artist. De Gheyn's fascination with the human figure, stimulated by Goltzius, became fully developed during his seven-year stay in Leiden between about 1595 and 1603. Leiden was then the center for anatomical study in Northern Europe, and there de Gheyn developed a strong interest in making studies of human anatomy and other scientific subjects. In all his work he showed a keen observation of reality.

De Gheyn's uninhibited and tender treatment of human subjects was a major accomplishment in the development of seventeenth-century Dutch art. In his drawing of the *Reclining Peasant*, his earlier mannerist style has given way to a new naturalism and monumentality in rendering the commonplace. De Gheyn creates volume and plasticity through his fully developed calligraphic style. Strong, thick lines create a powerful contrast against the light background. Stylized intertwining loops and rounded lines model form and composition. De Gheyn's nervous line and skillful use of shading give a sense of introspective emotion to the reclining figure. The youth's sensitive facial expression and relaxed pose display artistic vitality and observation of reality which anticipate the style of Rembrandt.

This drawing is to be included in a forthcoming book on de Gheyn by Professor J. Q. van Regteren Altena, who considers this to be a work of the artist's middle period (Sotheby Mak van Waay, June 9, 1975). Jacob Bean has stated in correspondence that a drawing bequeathed to The Metropolitan Museum by Harry B. Sperling is most probably an ink counter proof (with partly reinforced lines in pen and ink) of the verso.   R.M.

Marten van Heemskerck
Heemskerck near Haarlem 1498 – Haarlem 1574

48   The Triumph of Christ
184 x 260. Brown ink over black chalk; off-white paper; incised with

stylus for transfer. INSCR, pen and brown ink, lower r. edge: *Martinus va Heemskerck*; lower r. corner: *1559*; graphite, verso of old mount: *no 29 van Heemskerck*. PROV: R. Freiherr von Kühlmann; C. G. Boerner, Düsseldorf, Catalogue No. 60, Oct. 1972, no. 28

The Triumph of Christ, signed and dated 1559, is the last in a group of eight drawings made by Heemskerck for a series of prints entitled *The Triumph of Patience*, engraved by D. V. Coornhert and published by H. Cock (Hollstein, 1949–, VIII, 240, nos. 120–127, and Kerrich, 1829, p. 77, nos. 1–8). The eight engravings, placed side by side, were intended to imitate a procession led by Patience herself, followed by Isaac, Joseph, David, Job, Tobit, Saint Stephen, and Christ. These disparate Biblical figures, linked by the virtue of Patience defined here as the triumph over hardship through trust in and obedience to God, are presented as paradigms of faith and ethical behavior (Hoetinck, 1961). Heemskerck collaborated often with the engraver Coornhert (1522–1590), a prominent moralist and humanist, in the production of narrative allegories for such didactic purposes.

In the Steiner drawing, Christ is shown crowned and enthroned on the globe, with the four figures of the Apocalypse at the corners of his chariot. Like a triumphant emperor, he leads the enchained figures of the Devil, Death, the World, and Sin. The symbol for Sin is a conflation of animal elements traditionally associated with the Seven Deadly Sins, for example the dog's head representing Envy, the peacock's tail Pride. Other finished drawings for the series, the *Triumphs* of Isaac, Joseph, and Saint Stephen, are in the Boymans–van Beuningen Museum in Rotterdam (Hoetinck, 1961, figs. 9–11); the drawing for *Job* is in the Curtis O. Baer Collection (Baer, 1958, p. 28, fig. 15). The drawing for *Tobit* appeared in the same Boerner sale in 1972 and is reproduced in the catalogue (no. 27).

The foremost Romanist and Northern Mannerist of his generation, Heemskerck studied with Jan van Scorel (1495–1562), who had spent several years in Italy. In 1532, Heemskerck went to Rome himself, and made many drawings after the antique.   E.B.

48

Philips Koninck
Amsterdam 1619–1688

49 The Zaagmoelenpoort, Amsterdam

146 x 295. Pen and brush and brown ink and wash over black chalk, with accents of red chalk and white gouache; cream paper; retouches in the center windmill, repairs at l. edge and in vertical tear through pond into sky. INSCR, brown ink, lower r.: *Rembrandt*; verso: *Bij de Saagmolenspoort te Amsterdam*. PROV: unidentified blind collector's mark lower right (ⓒ); J. B. de Graff, 1820; J. P. Heseltine, Muller, Amsterdam, May 27–28, 1913, no. 134, pl. 16; Pieter Langerhuizen, Muller, Amsterdam, April 29, 1919, no. 252 (as Rembrandt school); Seligman and Co., New York, Dec. 1925, no. 41; H. E. ten Cate (Hannema, 1955, no. 249); B. Houthakker (1965, no. 36); Sotheby Mak van Waay, June 9, 1975, no. 83 (ill.). BIBL: Gerson, 1936, p. 65, Z1

This sheet contains many features characteristic of Koninck's early drawings dating from the 1650s. The compositional arrangement of a hill next to a body of water with a distant vista in the background is also found in two other drawings from the same period now in the Brussels museum (Gerson, 1936, Z22 and Z23). Typical of Koninck's early sheets are the predominantly brown tonality and the high horizon line. Later in his career, this master of the panoramic view varied his range of tone and lowered the horizon so that the sky often occupied two-thirds of the composition. Most of his pen drawings from the fifties are marked by the rigorous, wiry pen strokes found in the grass in the Steiner sheet, and the continuous, looping line used to describe the trees. The large open space in the foreground and the summary description of distant objects and figures reveal the influence on Koninck of Rembrandt's landscape drawings and etchings from the late forties and early fifties, even though Koninck may not have joined Rembrandt's school (ibid., p. 9).

Gerson attributes *The Zaagmoelenpoort* to Philips Koninck with some reservations (ibid., Z1). Yet the forceful penwork, as Seymour Slive pointed out in conversation, clearly shows the master's hand.

According to a map of Amsterdam dated 1650 (Lugt, 1920) the Zaagmoelenpoort, which means "gate of the sawmill," was located on the western perimeter of the city.   C.S.

Lagneau

Paris, 2nd half 16th century – early 17th century

50 Portrait of a Bearded Man in Doublet and Skull Cap

333 x 221. Black and red chalk with extensive stumping; buff paper; mounted. INSCR, pen and brown ink, lower r. corner: *100x*. PROV: Sunderland; J. P. Heseltine (L. 1507); Henry Oppenheimer, Christie's, July 10–14, 1936, no. 435; Roland, Browse, and Delbanco, London; Christie's, March 28, 1972, no. 27, pl. VI. BIBL: London, 1932, p. 331, no. 657; Commemoration Catalogue, 1932, p. 128, no. 569

Lagneau is a mysterious figure among French portraitists. No archival documents exist on his life and work. He is identified, on the basis of old inscriptions, with an impressive group of colored chalk drawings which portray members of the bourgeoisie and lower classes in a perceptive, sometimes caricatured, manner. Although these drawings are usually placed at the beginning of the seventeenth century, Benezit argues that one of them, in the Musée Carnavalet, is a portrait made from life of François Rabelais before the writer's death in 1553, and that the costumes also appear to date from the sixteenth century (Benezit, 1952, p. 37).

The drawings fall into three major stylistic groups. An album of portraits in the Cabinet des Estampes comes from the abbé Marcel de Marolles, in whose *Livre des Peintres* (1672) first mention is made of Lagneau. This album consists of extremely grotesque caricatures, generally executed in a dark and bold style (cf. Adhémar, 1973). This group contrasts with the more serious portraits which seem to be divided into two styles, some of them displaying a linear, and the others a softer, rubbed, almost painterly treatment. Both portrait types are calmer and more lightly executed than the album caricatures.

Examples of the softer type include two drawings from the Ian Woodner Collection (Woodner, 1971, nos. 56, 57); several of the fifteen Lagneaus from the Eugène Rodrigues Collection (Muller, Amsterdam, July 12–13, 1921, nos. 213–224); the *Portrait de vieillard* in the Musée de Dijon (Dijon, 1960, pl. 1); and the *Portrait d'homme au grand chapeau* in the Louvre (Lavallée, 1930, pl. 78).

1600 x

50

The Steiner drawing belongs to the linear type, which is also represented by a sheet in a German private collection (Stubbe, 1966, no. 154, pl. 69). By far the best stylistic comparison to the Steiner drawing is the slightly more caricatured *Old Man with Skull Cap* in the Walter C. Baker Collection (repr. *Arts Magazine*, Sept. 1960, p. 59). The two drawings are not only very similar in draughtsmanship but also in pose and costume details.

It has been argued by Pariset (1961) that only the caricatured drawings in the Marolles album are by Lagneau. Blunt (1973, p. 363) agrees in spirit with the limitation, emphasizing our total ignorance of the artist and concluding that the many sheets of high quality are "probably by several different artists, some working in Paris, others probably in Lorraine." On the other hand, Stubbe (1966) and Schab (Woodner, 1971) stress the unity of these sheets. In light of the link between the serious and the caricatured portraits, provided by the Baker and Steiner drawings, we might well accept the differences of style as the result of a development over a long lifetime.   N.H.

Nicolas Poussin
Les Andelys 1594 – Rome 1665

51   Trajan's Column, Studies of Details

306 x 223. Pen and brown ink and wash over traces of black chalk; off-white paper; lightly foxed; laid down. INSCR, graphite, verso backing paper: *Nicolas Poussin, Nº 2550 N. Poussin, 173a.* PROV: Lord Overstone (before 1878); C. Lloyd, Lockinge, Berkshire; Thos. Agnew and Sons, Ltd., London, 1967; J. D. Herring, New York. BIBL: Catalogue 1875–1877, p. 33, no. 140; Friedlaender and Blunt, 1939–1974, V, no. 331, pl. 248; Metropolitan Museum, 1976

This drawing is one of a group of detail studies from Trajan's Column which form a part of Nicolas Poussin's collection of copies after the antique. While it was previously assumed that Poussin drew these studies from plaster casts of the column (Reinhart, 1960, p. 26), Anthony Blunt has recently pointed out that the details correspond exactly to F. Villamena's engravings in Chacon (1576). Yet despite their derivation from engravings, the drawings possess

51

52

an independent sense of lively execution, described by William Pierson as a "bold, sketchy handling, [with] broad contrasts of light and shade, and the barest essentials of contour and structure, . . . [which create] a vivid and often dramatic momentary impression" (1942, p. 70).

Blunt also refers to Pietro Santi Bartoli's engravings (1673) in order to identify each component of the drawing. The group of figures at the bottom of the sheet represent the emperor Trajan (left) being presented with a captured spy during the first Dacian war (Chacon, 1576, pl. 16; Bartoli, 1673, pl. 13; Froehner, 1872, p. 7 and I, pl. 42). The prows of two galleys (top left) come from an episode of river navigation, also during the first Dacian war (Chacon, 1576, pl. 31; Bartoli, 1673, pl. 25; Froehner, 1872, p. 11 and II, pl. 59). The soldiers on horseback (top right) are members of Trajan's entourage as he approaches the Dacians who are surrendering their children, from the second Dacian war (Chacon, 1576, pl. 78; Bartoli, 1673, pl. 66; Froehner, 1872, p. 18 and III, pl. 119).

The studies from Trajan's Column were dated to the late thirties or early forties by Sir Anthony Blunt. There can be no doubt, however, that the very abstract and geometric outlines, frequently breaking up into small strokes, and the planar conception of the figures stressed by the washes comprise a style close to that of drawings for the second series of the *Sacraments*, for example the *Confirmation*, ca. 1645 (Friedlaender and Blunt, 1939–1974, I, no. 87). Therefore the drawings most likely date from after Poussin's sojourn in Paris of 1640–1642.   N.H.

Rembrandt Harmensz. van Rijn
Leiden 1606 – Amsterdam 1669

52   Nathan Admonishing David

126 x 149. Pen and brown ink; cream paper; indented for transfer.
PROV: C. Ploos van Amstel (L. 3002–3004, L. 2034), sale, Amsterdam, March 3, 1800, I, no. 15; J. Jacobsz. de Vos (L. 1450); G. Schöffer; A. W. M. Mensing, sale, Amsterdam, April 27–29, 1937, no. 558; Frits Lugt; C. R. Rudolf, Sotheby Mak van Waay, April 18, 1977, no. 106.
BIBL: Valentiner, 1925–1934, no. 166; Benesch, 1935, p. 51; Royal

Academy, 1953, no. 301; Benesch, 1954–1957, no. 918, fig. 1129; Rudolf, 1962, no. 123; Benesch, 1973, no. 918, fig. 1195

The figures in this drawing were etched early in the eighteenth century by Matthys Pool as part of a group of twelve reproductions of drawings by Rembrandt (Wurzbach, 1906, II, 447, no. 6), including the study of the same subject in Berlin (Benesch, 1973, no. 947).

The only writer who has had any reservations about the Steiner drawing's authenticity was Wilhelm Valentiner, but it was accepted without hesitation by Benesch. Like Benesch, Seymour Slive (in correspondence) firmly endorsed the original attribution to Rembrandt and praised the high quality of this drawing.

Comparison with *Homer Reciting* (ibid., no. 913) of 1652 confirms Benesch's dating of the Steiner *Nathan and David* to about 1652–1653. Both works share the angular, brittle pen line and delicate diagonal hatching characteristic of Rembrandt's style at this time; the attitude of the prophet reflects the pose of Homer in reverse. The watermark in the Steiner sheet (Churchill, 1935, no. 355) also corroborates the approximate date assigned to it by Benesch. Rembrandt printed impressions of the etchings *Saint Jerome Reading in an Italian Landscape* (Hind, 1923, no. 267) of about 1653–1654, *Christ at Emmaeus* (ibid., no. 282) of 1654, and *Jan Lutma* (ibid., no. 290) of 1656 on papers bearing this watermark (Stampfle, 1969, p. 181, no. 15).

The scene is from 2 Samuel 12:1–14. King David has seduced Bathsheba, the wife of the soldier Uriah. Bathsheba conceives a child and David, who wants to make her his wife, orders Uriah to the front line of battle, where he is killed fighting for his king. The Lord sends the prophet Nathan to David, to tell a parable revealing the enormity of his sin. David repents, and the Lord forgives him, but the child conceived in adultery is cursed and dies.

This kind of theme appealed to Rembrandt because it allowed him to capture the instant when the protagonist experiences a new state of awareness or an unexpected insight. The king's pained expression and the gesture of his right hand suggest that Rembrandt has chosen the moment where David suddenly recognizes the full significance of the prophet's words and becomes conscious of the gravity and the implications of his transgression.

Four drawings by Rembrandt showing Nathan's visit to David have survived. One sheet (Benesch, 1973, no. 890) depicts a slightly earlier event in the narrative, while the Steiner drawing and two other versions (ibid., nos. 947 and 948), both dated by Benesch about 1654–1655, focus on the king's response to Nathan's message. In the latter three works David is richly dressed and Rembrandt includes the crown and sceptre, symbols of his power. The attributes of wealth and authority may allude to Nathan's castigation of David for sinning against the Lord, who bestowed upon him the kingdom of Israel. Both figures are seated in the two later drawings, the king on a low dais and the prophet a little beneath him. The Berlin version (ibid., no. 947) seems to depict the same moment as the Steiner sheet. In the Metropolitan Museum drawing (ibid., no. 948) the instant of recognition is already past. David now wears a wistful, pensive, and sad expression of grief and remorse.   w.w.r.

Roelant Roghman
Amsterdam 1597? – ca. 1686

53   Wooded River Landscape

457 x 325. Pen and brown ink and grey wash with accents of white gouache; cream paper. INSCR, brown ink: *Roelant Roghman*. PROV: Sotheby Mak van Waay, May 3, 1976, no. 172 (ill.)

Practically nothing is known about the life of Roelant Roghman. According to Houbraken (1718, I, 173–174), he was born in Amsterdam in 1597. However, his earliest surviving works, dated 1646, suggest that his birthdate may have been somewhat later. Roghman is assumed to have been active in Amsterdam for two reasons: because he is said to have been a "great friend" of Rembrandt, and because it is recorded that he was in Amsterdam in 1661 and 1664.

The signature on the Steiner drawing matches those on others by Roghman, who is best known for hilly landscapes and Italianate scenes, marked by large summary splashes of wash and dramatic contrasts of light and dark. This drawing, however, is related technically to a different aspect of Roghman's oeuvre—his more than 240 large drawings of cities, castles, and country villas. The Steiner

53

drawing is similar to these in its size, finished quality, application of washes and pen, and treatment of foliage (see van Regteren Altena and Ward-Jackson, 1970, no. 18). Dates on several of Roghman's city and castle drawings indicate that he did two groups of them, one around 1646–1649 and another around 1654. Those from 1654 seem to lack the calligraphic flourishes found in both the earlier series and in his loose landscape sketches. Such flourishes in brown ink in the foreground of the Steiner drawing suggest that it may date to the earlier period.   N.N.

Peter Paul Rubens
Siegen 1577 – Antwerp 1640

54   Study of the Head of a Woman

258 x 193. Black and red chalk; white paper; reworked by a later hand. PROV: Jonkheer Goll von Franckenstein (L. 2987); William Stirling, Esq.; Sotheby's, Oct. 21, 1963, no. 39 (ill.); Norton Simon Collection, Parke Bernet, May 8, 1971, no. 200A (ill.). BIBL: Royal Academy, 1938, no. 613 (ill.)

This drawing appears to have been a study for the head of the Virgin in the oil painting *The Virgin and Child* attributed to Rubens, formerly in the collection of Anthony de Rothschild and now in the Ascot Collection of the British National Trust (Royal Academy, 1938, fig. 67). Minor details of the hair and the relationship between the ear and hairline have been altered in the painting. Reporting a notation on the mount, in pencil, that the model was Isabella Brant, Rubens' first wife, Sotheby's catalogue argues in favor of Rubens' sister-in-law Susanne Fourment, whom the artist portrayed on a sheet in the Boymans–van Beuningen Museum in Rotterdam (Held, 1959, fig. 114, cat. no. 104). However, the thin, cheerfully upturned lips, slightly broken nose, double chin, and straggly eyebrows visible in the Steiner drawing are very definitely present in the British Museum portrait drawing of Isabella Brant (ibid., fig. 115, cat. no. 103), and the style of the Steiner drawing is close to Rubens' drawings around 1619–1622 (ibid., nos. 98, 103), when he was married to her. Yet Rubens always had in mind an ideal female type, and this obscures the identity of his models.

The authenticity of the drawing has been challenged. Unquestioned as the work of the master in previous publications, the Parke Bernet sales catalogue lists the drawing as "attributed to Sir Peter Paul Rubens." Most scholars who have since inspected the work have been reluctant to attribute the drawing with certainty to the hand of Rubens. However, the sheet is not obviously the work of Rubens' students and exhibits greater quality than known copies.

This head, trimmed all around, should be viewed in the context of Rubens' preparatory studies related to paintings rather than in that of his brilliant portraits. Works such as two study sheets in the Albertina and one formerly in a Stettin private collection (Burchard and d'Hulst, 1963, nos. 157, 187, 158) also downplay light and surface qualities. Yet when compared with these sheets, the outlines and shading of the Steiner drawing are hesitant and heavy, apparently betraying a hand other than that of Rubens. Since the quick strokes of the background and some areas of the hair in fact do resemble the master's sketching style, it can be surmised that the drawing is a heavily reworked sheet by Rubens.   A.K.

Cornelis Saftleven
Gorkum 1607 – Rotterdam 1681

55   Country Woman

210 x 165. Black chalk; cream paper; on verso, traces of black chalk, drawing illegible; extensive restoration of corners, watermark: large double eagle. INSCR, graphite, verso, lower center: (Nr2); No. 4227 C. PROV: illegible traces of pink collector's stamp on lower r. corner; Dr. Pollak, Rome; Kurt Meissner, Zurich

Cornelis Saftleven, son and pupil of Herman the Elder and brother of the artist Herman Saftleven, is known for his portrayal of simple peasant life in the high Baroque period of seventeenth-century Dutch art. A talented and versatile draughtsman, he also showed a keen interest in rendering studies of domestic and exotic animals. Particularly impressive, however, are his studies of young boys and older men and women depicted in a variety of relaxed poses.

54

55

This drawing, attributed orally to Saftleven by Frits Lugt and E. Haverkamp-Begemann, demonstrates Saftleven's special talent for conveying a vital warmth and intimacy to his figure studies. The woman, sitting slightly forward in her chair with her hands resting comfortably on her lap, seems about to break into a broad smile. The folds of her dress are drawn with modulating tones of dark and light contained within thick outlines. This fresh and controlled drawing is attentive to subtle details of dress such as the head scarf, where tight, nervous lines create convincing folds terminating in a knot tied behind the figure's neck. In all of his figure studies Saftleven showed keen observation and an interest in peasant costume and psychology.

It is difficult to place this undated drawing in the chronology of Saftleven's work. Bolten (1967, p. 116) notes that "a great number of Saftleven's drawings bear a date. Through these dates it is apparent that Saftleven's style has not changed significantly in the course of several decades." Based on stylistic comparisons with many of his dated drawings, however, it seems most likely that this work falls into the period of the 1630s.   R.M.

Jan Tengnagel
Amsterdam 1565–1629

56 Abraham Visited by the Angels

336 x 235. Black chalk, pen and brown ink, brown washes, touches of graphite added in the faces of the angels, border by the artist; white paper; laid down. INSCR, verso: *Colnagy Collection.* PROV: Colnagy; Herbert E. Feist Gallery, May 1973, no. 35. BIBL: Sumowski, 1975; Robinson, 1977, no. 12

Jan Tengnagel and his brothers-in-law Jan and Jacob Pynas and Pieter Lastman were members of a group of Dutch artists called the Pre-Rembrandtists. In the first decade of the seventeenth century they went to Rome, where they came under the influence of the German-born Elsheimer. Back in Amsterdam, the Pre-Rembrandtists founded a school of history painting which replaced the old style of Mannerism with a new feeling of light, space, and more natural forms.

Abraham Visited by the Angels is a fine example of the Pre-Rembrandtist style in early seventeenth-century Dutch art. A group of figures is closely arranged in a setting of ample space. A sense of volume and perspective is created through the device of alternating patterns of light and shade. Lines are skillfully used to create a rich decorative effect, almost giving the appearance of a stage setting. Some mannerist holdovers remain in the forced posing of the angels and tight, looping strokes on the tree limbs.

This drawing, once attributed to Pieter Lastman, was at first connected by Werner Sumowski with the work of Lambert Jacobsz. More recently, however, the same writer has given the drawing to Tengnagel (Sumowski, 1975, pp. 171–175). This opinion is also shared by Franklin Robinson (Robinson, 1977). Robinson places strong emphasis on the gesturing of Abraham's hands to express emotion, and the peculiar calligraphy used to outline foliage as being typical artistic devices for Tengnagel. He also makes comparisons with the Tengnagel paintings *Jacob and Rachel*, 1615 (Tümpel, 1974, p. 23), and *Vertumnus and Pomona*, 1619 (ibid., p. 24), pointing out stylistic similarities to the firm outlines set against Italian landscapes. Of these two, *Jacob and Rachel* is more convincing in showing firmness and rigidity, similar to the Steiner drawing, which otherwise seems to be lacking in his paintings.

Drawings attributed to Tengnagel are extremely rare. This work, by far the most monumental, elaborate, and finished of Tengnagel's sheets, is unusual in his known oeuvre.   R.M.

David Teniers the Younger
Antwerp 1610 – Brussels 1690

57   Studies of Hounds

190 x 320. Graphite; white paper. PROV: unidentified armorial collector's mark (L. 2697); Sir Francis Mackenzie, fifth baronet of Gairloch; Madam Mackenzie of Gairloch; Christie's, March 19, 1975, no. 81 (ill.)

That David Teniers was one of the most popular genre painters of his day is affirmed by his position as court painter both to Leopold

56

Wilhelm and his successor, Don Juan of Austria. Teniers' works were influenced by his father-in-law Jan Brueghel the Elder, and afterwards by Adriaen Brouwer (Vlieghe, 1961–1966, pp. 124–130). Primarily in graphite, Teniers' drawings are characteristically sketched in short flowing strokes, often punctuated by knots of line.

The Steiner study resembles several sketches by Teniers on sheets of similar size with figures or animals scattered about the page. These are in the drawing cabinets of Berlin (inv. 12024; Bock and Rosenberg, 1930, I, 280), London (Hind, 1923, II, 137, nos. 1 and 2), and Stockholm (inv. 2121/1863; Bernt, 1958, no. 563). Of this group, the last, a study of *Two Hunters, a Peasant, and Dogs*, is closest to the Steiner sheet in subject and in execution. Carlos van Hasselt has dated this group of drawings to around 1660–1663 (Hasselt, 1972, p. 137).

While the Steiner sketch cannot be directly related to a painting by Teniers, hunters and hounds appear in several of his works, including *Trees in a Valley*, Leningrad (Smdskaya, 1962, no. 67); *Country Scene*, Lierre, St. Gommaire; and *Landscape with Hunting Party*, in Petworth House, Sussex, England.   A.A.

Lucas van Uden
Antwerp 1595–1632

58   Trees

347 x 225. Pen and brown ink, grey wash, and watercolor over graphite; white paper; fingerprint in blue ink, crease, four corners made up. INSCR, blue ballpoint ink, verso: *26*; one unidentifiable paraph. PROV: Schaeffer Galleries

Lucas van Uden is known for his landscape views of Flanders, and particularly for his watercolor and pen and ink drawings in which his talents seem demonstrated to their best advantage. Though probably tutored by his little-known father, Artus van Uden, he was greatly influenced by Peter Paul Rubens and possibly Jan Brueghel the Elder.

Two major types of works stand out in his oeuvre: large pan-

58

oramic views of hills and flatlands, and compositions dominated by groups of trees. Carlos van Hasselt has recently shown that many works of the latter group can be dated to the 1640s on the basis of inscriptions by the artist on some of them ranging from 1640 to 1649 (Hasselt, 1972, p. 144, n. 4). Some of these sheets are extremely close to the Steiner drawing in that they show a few birches or beech trees on a bluff in the foreground, silhouetted against an evening sky and with an expanse of land in the background. Van Hasselt singles these out for their special charm; indeed, the silvery light and delicate stroke and coloring typical of van Uden are here in total accord with the delicate bark and clear shape of the trees and the misty light of the sky. Particularly close to the Steiner study are a sheet in the Fondation Custodia in Paris (ibid., no. 111) and one in Hamburg (Bernt, 1958, II, pl. 5). Others like it are in Rotterdam (Hasselt, 1974, no. 112, pl. 130) and in the Fitzwilliam Museum in Cambridge, England (Hasselt, 1961, nos. 86a, 87, fig. 28 [then in the Bruce Ingram Collection]).   J.J.

Willem van de Velde the Younger
Leiden 1633 – London 1707

59   Frigate at Anchor

159 x 221. Pen and brown ink with grey wash; cream paper. PROV: Earl of Warwick (L. 2600); J. P. Heseltine (L. 1507); P. & D. Colnaghi, 1912; Robin Lehmann; P. & D. Colnaghi, *Old Master Drawings*, June 27 – July 29, 1972, no. 43 (ill.). BIBL: Heseltine, 1910, no. 34 (ill.)

This drawing is a characteristic work by Willem van de Velde the Younger. As a marine painter and draughtsman he followed in the tradition of his father, Willem van de Velde the Elder, and of his teacher, Simon de Vlieger. In general, the younger van de Velde's drawings fall into three subject categories: historical naval encounters, ship portraits, and seascapes of which the Steiner drawing is an example. In this drawing of a calm at sea, the frigates and barges are

set in three successive receding planes. The large frigate in the right foreground dries its sails while firing a salute to a nearby yacht. The cursory, scratchy, but sure draughtsmanship and minimal attention to detail distinguish the Steiner drawing from van de Velde's early drawings and place it around 1700. At this time van de Velde did several other drawings in the same medium of pen and brown ink with grey washes (see Robinson, 1958, nos. 714 and 715). As in all of his drawings from this period, the washes are used for the most part to accentuate and fill out the penwork, and therefore are more limited in function than in his early drawings.   N.N.

Tobias Verhaecht
Antwerp 1561–1631

60   Wooded Landscape with Stag Hunt

211 x 393. Pen and brown ink, brown wash over black chalk; cream paper. INSCR, ink, recto: *Mattheus Brille*. PROV: Sotheby's, Nov. 22, 1974, no. 21; Yvonne Tan-Bunzl

As a draughtsman, Verhaecht is best known for his imposing alpine panoramas with rugged cliffs and towering pines. The eccentric pen technique—short parallel or zigzag lines punctuated by innumerable dots—lends to these drawings an abstract, rigid quality. At least three of these mountain vistas are dated between 1616 and 1620 (Metropolitan Museum, New York, inv. 58.72, 1616; Hermitage, Leningrad, inv. 15090, 1617; Kunsthalle, Hamburg, inv. 22636, 1620), and it seems likely that this tight, abstracting style is characteristic of Verhaecht's mature years.

The *Landscape with Stag Hunt* belongs to another group of drawings which share its looser execution and relatively spontaneous approach, and probably date from Verhaecht's Italian sojourn in the 1580s or shortly after his return to Antwerp in 1591. Related works are preserved in the British Museum (Popham, 1932, p. 187, no. 3), the Hessisches Landesmuseum, Darmstadt (inv. AE428 and AE563), the Fogg Art Museum (acc. no. 1969.109), and in an anonymous private collection (Prybram-Gladona, 1969, no. 104). Another was sold at Sotheby's, November 22, 1974 (no. 29).

In the Steiner sheet, the impulsive zigzag stroke of the pen, the bold contrasts achieved by the application of the wash, and the handling of the foliage and clouds depend upon the style of Lodewijk Toeput, called Pozzoserrato. Verhaecht encountered Pozzoserrato's drawings either in Italy or in the Antwerp studio of Toeput's pupil Joos de Momper. Comparable works by Pozzoserrato are in the Fondation Custodia, Paris (Institut Néerlandais, 1974, no. 81, dated 1582), and the Biblioteca Nacional, Madrid (Franz, 1969, I, 308; II, fig. 452, probably from the 1580s, not ca. 1600 as suggested by Franz). The earliest datable drawings by Verhaecht are a study in the Kunsthalle, Bremen (inv. 7254), related to the painting *Saint John on Patmos* of 1598 (Hermitage, 1958, II, 45, fig. 36); *The Death of Aeschylus* (no. 61 in this exhibition); and the *Jonah and the Whale* (Berlin, 1975, no. 275), which on the basis of its similarities to the other two should also be dated around 1600. Comparison of this group with the mountain panoramas of 1616–1620 indicates that the free, spontaneous manner derived from Pozzoserrato steadily rigidifies as the artist matures. Verhaecht's works of 1598 – ca. 1606 exhibit the relatively low viewpoint and the formulae for describing rocks and foliage employed in the *Landscape with Stag Hunt*. However, the pen technique of the *Saint John on Patmos* of 1598 is already tighter and further removed from Toeput's loose handling than in the sheet exhibited. It therefore seems reasonable to assume that the Steiner drawing belongs to a still earlier period, ca. 1585–1595.

W.W.R.

61   The Death of Aeschylus

Diam. 255. Pen and brown ink with brown and blue washes accented with white gouache; cream paper; scratched in various places to make highlights and corrections; watermark: elephant, similar to Briquet no. 5949. INSCR, graphite, verso of secondary support, lower edge: *Mompre .20*; *Verhaecht RPRF*. PROV: Henri Leroux, sale,

61

Hôtel Droûot, May 21, 1968, no. 53; Paul Prouté, Paris. BIBL: Stechow, 1975

An old inscription on the verso indicates that this drawing was once attributed to Joos de Momper. Only in the last fifty years have Verhaecht's drawings been separated from the work of his contemporary; the attribution of the Steiner sheet to Verhaecht was established conclusively by Wolfgang Stechow (1975). Verhaecht's drawings have also been confused with those of his student and imitator, Pieter van Houck. As Wolfgang Wegner was first to point out (orally), van Houck made an exact copy, signed and dated 1606, of the Steiner Verhaecht, which has proven instrumental in establishing a relative date for the original. This is significant because very few of Verhaecht's drawings are securely dated. As Stechow points out, the Steiner Verhaecht, in conjunction with the van Houck copy, provides an important anchor for a chronology of Verhaecht's oeuvre.

Before the Steiner sheet came to light, Stechow's publication of the van Houck copy in 1929 (p. 45) prompted H. Gerson to attribute to van Houck drawings which had previously been given to Verhaecht. Through the discovery of the Steiner landscape, drawings such as the *Jonah and the Whale* in Berlin (Berlin, 1975, no. 275, pl. 237), which is very close to our drawing in dimension, shape, and style, have been returned to Verhaecht.

The van Houck sheet bears an inscription which indicates that it was to serve as a design for a stained-glass roundel. Stechow deduces that the Verhaecht model was intended for the same purpose.

The scene depicted is the death of the Greek writer-philosopher Aeschylus, who was killed by a tortoise dropped upon his head by an eagle. In this composition, however, Verhaecht clearly subordinates this episode to the depiction of an imaginative and decorative landscape, intended to portray the city of Syracuse with Mount Aetna.

E.B.

Marten de Vos
Antwerp 1532–1603

62 Emperor Ninus

206 x 260. Pen and brown ink and wash over black chalk, traces of
squaring underneath; cream paper; paper cracked following outline
of watermark: armorial with eagle, similar to Briquet no. 224.
INSCR, brown ink, verso, center of top edge: *Ninus.* PROV: Paul
Grigaut; private collection, New York; Joellyn Duesberry

Emperor Ninus is the design for the first in a series of four prints
depicting victorious antique rulers, engraved by Adriaen Collaert
and published by Philip Galle (Hollstein, 1949–, IV, 204, nos. 433–
436). According to legend, Ninus was the founder of the city of Nin-
eveh and conquered all of western Asia in seventeen years, establishing the first empire. Here he is shown symbolically trampling a defeated ruler. Ninus is followed in the series by the next conqueror,
Cyrus the Great, who is in turn succeeded by Alexander the Great
and Julius Caesar. Each hero carries his own distinctive banner. Cyrus
is shown treading on a monarch whose lion banner is like the one
carried by Ninus in the Steiner drawing; Alexander is depicted
defeating two kings with the banners of Ninus and Cyrus; and
beneath the feet of Caesar's horse lie three defeated men and the
banners associated with all three of the preceding rulers in the series.

Marten de Vos was the son and student of Peter de Vos. He later
studied with the foremost Romanist in Antwerp, Frans Floris (1516–
1570). After his apprenticeship with Floris, de Vos traveled to Italy,
where he visited Rome and Florence and worked in Venice with
Tintoretto (Wurzbach, 1910, II, 820). One of the most respected
masters in Antwerp, de Vos was a prolific draughtsman, and although he made many paintings, almost all of his known drawings
are related to designs for prints (Reinsch, 1967, p. 4). His fertile
imagination was ideally suited to the allegorical and Biblical prints
which were popular at the time. This drawing is a beautiful example
of the pictorial richness of his inventions.　　E.B.

Bibliography

ADHÉMAR, 1973

Adhémar, J. "Les portraits dessinés du XVIe siècle au Cabinet des Estampes, deuxième partie." *Gazette des Beaux-Arts* LXXXII (Dec. 1973): 341–349.

ADIMARI, 1706

Adimari, Lodovico. *Prose sacre contenenti il compendio della vita di S. Maria Maddalena de' Pazzi, e la relazione delle feste fatte in Firenze per la sua canonizazione con un discorso della Passione del Redentore.* Florence, 1706.

AMBROSOLI, 1906

Ambrosoli, Solone. *Atlante numismatico italiano (Monete moderne).* Milan, 1906.

ASKEW, 1966

Askew, Pamela. "Perino del Vaga's Decorations for the Palazzo Doria, Genoa." *The Burlington Magazine* XCVIII (1956): 46–53.

BAER, 1958

Drawings from the Collection of Curtis O. Baer. Cambridge, Mass.: Fogg Art Museum, 1958

BAGLIONE, 1642

Baglione, Giovanni. *Le vite de' pittori, scultori, architetti, ed intagliatori dal pontificato di Gregorio XIII del 1572, fino a' tempi di papa Urbano VIII nel 1642.* Facsimile ed. Rome, 1935.

BAGLIONE, 1733

————. *Le vite de' pittori, scultori, architetti, ed intagliatori, del pontificato di Gregorio XIII del 1572 fino a' tempi di papa Urbano VIII nel 1642.* Naples, 1733.

BAROCCHI, *DISEGNI*, 1964

Barocchi, P. *Mostra di disegni del Vasari e della sua cerchia.* Florence: Galleria degli Uffizi, 1964.

BAROCCHI, *PITTORE*, 1964

————. *Vasari pittore.* Milan, 1964.

BARTOLI, 1673

Bartoli, Pietro S. *Colonna Traiana.* Rome, 1673.

BATTISTI, 1954

Battisti, Eugenio. "Profilo del Gobbo dei Carracci." *Commentari* V (1954): 290–302.

BEAN, 1966

Bean, Jacob. *Italian Drawings in the Art Museum, Princeton University*. New York, 1966.

BELTRAMI, 1916

Beltrami, Luca. *Disegni di Giusto Aurelio Meissonier, Artista italiano alla corte di Luigi XIV*. Milan, 1916.

BENESCH, 1928

Benesch, Otto. *Die Zeichnungen der Niederländischen Schulen des XV. und XVI. Jahrhunderts*. Vienna, 1928.

BENESCH, 1935

————. *Rembrandt, Werk und Forschung*. Vienna, 1935.

BENESCH, 1954–1957

————. *The Drawings of Rembrandt, A Critical and Chronological Catalogue*. 6 vols. London, 1954–1957.

BENESCH, 1973

————. *The Drawings of Rembrandt. Complete Edition in Six Volumes*. Enlarged and edited by E. Benesch. 6 vols. New York, 1973.

BENEZIT, 1952

Benezit, Emmanuel. *Dictionnaire critique et documentaire des peintres, sculpteurs, dessinateurs, et graveurs*. S.v. "Lagneau." 1952.

BENEZIT, 1976

————. *Dictionnaire des peintres, sculpteurs, dessinateurs, et graveurs*. S.v. "Canuti." 3rd ed., 1976.

BERENSON, 1938

Berenson, Bernard. *The Drawings of the Florentine Painters*. 3 vols., amplified edition. Chicago, 1938.

BERGAMO, 1962

Disegni dell'Accademia Carrara di Bergamo. Venice, 1962.

BERLIN, 1975

Pieter Bruegel d. Ä. als Zeichner. Berlin: Kupferstichkabinett Berlin, 1975.

BERNT, 1958

Bernt, W. *Die Niederländischen Zeichner des 17. Jahrhunderts*. 2 vols. Munich, 1958.

BIERENS DE HAAN, 1948

Bierens de Haan, J. C. J. *L'Oeuvre gravé de Cornelis Cort*. The Hague, 1948.

BLANKERT, 1975

Blankert, Albert. *Kunst als Regeringszaak in Amsterdam in de 17 eeuw; rondom schilderijen van Ferdinand Bol*. Lochem, Holland, 1975.

157

BLUNT, 1954

Blunt, Anthony. *The Drawings of Giovanni Benedetto Castiglione and Stefano della Bella in the Collection of Her Majesty the Queen at Windsor Castle.* London, 1954.

BLUNT, 1973

———. "Drawings at Waddesdon Manor." *Master Drawings* XI (1973): 359–364.

BLUNT AND COOKE, 1960

Blunt, Anthony, and Cooke, Hereward Lester. *The Roman Drawings of the XVII and XVIII Centuries in the Collection of Her Majesty the Queen at Windsor Castle.* London, 1960.

BOCK AND ROSENBERG, 1930

Bock, E., and Rosenberg, J. *Staatliche Museum zu Berlin, Die Niederländischen Meister.* Vol. 1. Berlin, 1930.

BODMER, 1934

Bodmer, Heinrich. "Drawings by the Carracci: An Aesthetic Analysis." *Old Master Drawings* VIII (March 1934): 151–166.

BODMER, 1939

———. *Ludovico Carracci.* Magdeburg, 1939.

BOLOGNA, 1956

Mostra dei Carracci. Catalogo Critico. Bologna, 1956.

BOLTEN, 1967

Bolten, J. *Dutch Drawings from the Collection of Dr. C. Hofstede deGroot.* Utrecht, 1967.

BOREA, 1965

Borea, Evelina. *Domenichino.* Milan, 1965.

BURKE, 1976

Burke, James D. *Jan Both: Paintings, Drawings, and Prints.* New York, 1976.

BURCHARD AND D'HULST, 1963

Burchard, L., and d'Hulst, R.-A., *Rubens' Drawings.* 2 vols. Brussels, 1963.

CECCHELLI, 1928

Cecchelli, Carlo. *Il Vaticano.* Milan and Rome, 1928.

CHACON, 1576

Chacon, Alfonso. *Historia utriusque belli Dacici a Traiano Caesare gesti, ex simulachris quae in columna eiusdem Romae visuntur collecta.* Rome, 1576.

CHIARINI, 1972

Chiarini, Marco. *I Disegni Italiani di Paesaggio dal 1600 al 1750.* Treviso, 1972.

CHIARINI, 1975
————. S.v. "Cantagallina" in *Dizionario biografico degli Italiani*. Rome, 1975.

CHURCHILL, 1935
Churchill, W. A. *Watermarks of the XVII and XVIII Centuries*. Amsterdam, 1935.

CLARK, 1963
Clark, Anthony M. "Pierleone Ghezzi's Portraits." *Paragone* XIV, no. 165 (Sept. 1963): 11–21.

CLARK, 1974
————. "Three Ghezzis." *Minneapolis Institute of Arts Bulletin* LX (1971–1973): 62–67.

COCKE, 1972
Cocke, Richard. *Pier Francesco Mola*. Oxford, 1972.

COLNAGHI, 1959
Loan Exhibition of Drawings by Old Masters from the Collection of Dr. and Mrs. Francis Springell. London: P. & D. Colnaghi, 1959.

COLNAGHI, 1971
Loan Exhibition of Drawings by Old Masters from the Collection of Mr. Geoffrey Gathorne-Hardy. London: P. & D. Colnaghi, 1971.

COLNAGHI, 1972
Exhibition of Old Master Drawings. London: P. & D. Colnaghi, 1972.

COMMEMORATION CATALOGUE, 1932
Commemoration Catalogue of the Exhibition of French Art 1200–1900. London, 1932.

COX-REARICK, 1971
Cox-Rearick, Janet. "Dessins de Bronzino pour la Chapelle d'Eleonora au Palazzo Vecchio." *Revue de l'Art*, no. 14 (1971): 6–22.

DATTENBERG, 1940
Dattenberg, H. "Lambert Doomer als Zeichner." *Pantheon* XXV (1940): 13–16.

DAVIDSON, 1966
Davidson, Bernice. *Mostra di Disegni di Perino del Vaga*. Florence: Galleria degli Uffizi, 1966.

DAVIES, 1973
Davies, Alice. "Allaert van Everdingen." Ph.D. dissertation, Harvard University, 1973.

DETROIT-FLORENCE, 1974
The Twilight of the Medici: Late Baroque Art in Florence, 1670–1743. Detroit: The Detroit Institute; Florence: Palazzo Pitti, 1974.

DEVESME, 1971
DeVesme, Alexandre. *Stefano della Bella. Catalogue Raisonné*. Reprint from *Le Peintre-graveur Italien* (1906) with introduction and additions by Phyllis Dearborn Massar. New York, 1971.

DIJON, 1960
Dessins français XVIIe et XVIIIe siècles des collections du Musée de Dijon. Dijon: Musée de Dijon, 1960.

DOWLEY, 1957
Dowley, Francis H. "Some Maratta Drawings at Düsseldorf." *The Art Quarterly* XX (Summer 1957): 163–179.

DUSSLER, 1966
Dussler, Luitpold. *Raffael, Kritisches Verzeichnis der Gemälde, Wandbilder und Bildteppiche*. Munich, 1966.

EDINBURGH, 1965
Old Master Drawings from the Collection of Dr. and Mrs. Francis Springell. Edinburgh: National Gallery of Scotland, 1965.

EDINBURGH, 1969
Italian 16th-Century Drawings from British Private Collections. Edinburgh: Edinburgh Festival Society and Scottish Arts Council, 1969.

EDINBURGH, 1972
Italian 17th-Century Drawings from British Private Collections. Edinburgh: Arts Council, 1972.

EISLER, 1963
Eisler, Colin. *Drawings of the Masters, Flemish and Dutch Drawings*. New York, 1963.

ELLESMERE, 1898
Catalogue of the Ellesmere Collection of Drawings at Bridgewater House. London, 1898.

FAGGIN, 1965
Faggin, G. T. "De genre-schilder Marten van Cleef." *Oud Holland* LXXX (1965): 34–46.

FEINBLATT, 1952
Feinblatt, Ebria. "The Roman Work of Domenico Maria Canuti." *Art Quarterly* XV (1952): 45–65.

FEINBLATT, 1961
———. "Some Drawings by Canuti Identified." *Art Quarterly* XXIV (1961): 262–282.

FEIST, 1973

European Drawings. New York: Herbert E. Feist Gallery, 1973.

FRANZ, 1969

Franz, H. G. *Niederländische Landschaftsmalerei im Zeitalter des Manierismus.* Graz, 1969.

FREEDBERG, 1951

Freedberg, Sydney J. *Parmigianino.* Cambridge, Mass., 1951.

FREEDBERG, 1971

————. *Painting in Italy 1500–1600.* Hammondsworth, Middlesex, 1971.

FRIEDLAENDER AND BLUNT, 1939–1974

Friedlaender, Walter, and Blunt, Anthony. *The Drawings of Nicolas Poussin.* 5 vols. London, 1939–1974.

FROEHNER, 1872–1874

Froehner, Wilhelm. *La Colonne Trajane.* Edited by J. Rothschild. With 4 vols. plates. Paris, 1872–1874.

VON DER GABELENTZ, 1922

Gabelentz, Hans von der. *Fra Bartolommeo und die Florentiner Renaissance.* 2 vols. Leipzig, 1922.

GATHORNE-HARDY, 1902

A Descriptive Catalogue of Drawings in the Possession of the Hon. A. E. Gathorne-Hardy. London, 1902.

VAN GELDER, 1970

Gelder, J. G. van. "Lambert ten Cate als Kunstverzamelaar." *Nederlands Kunsthistorisch Jaarboek* XXII (1970), 139–186.

VAN GELDER, 1973

————. "Frühe Rembrandt Sammlungen." In *Neue Beiträge zur Rembrandt-Forschung,* edited by O. van Simson and J. Kelch. Berlin, 1973.

GERE, 1963

Gere, John A. "Taddeo Zuccaro as a Designer of Maiolica." *The Burlington Magazine* CV (1963): 306–315.

GERE, 1969

————. *Taddeo Zuccaro: His Development Studies in His Drawings.* London, 1969.

GERSON, 1936

Gerson, Horst. *Philips Koninck.* Berlin, 1936.

GERSON, 1954

————. "Probleme der Rembrandtschule." *Kunstchronik* X (1954): 121–124.

GERSON, 1965

———. "Bredius 447." In *Festschrift für Dr. Edouard Trautscholdt.* Hamburg, 1965.

GIAMPAOLO, *ANTICHITÀ VIVA*, 1974

Giampaolo, Mario di. "Disegni Bolognesi dal XVI al XVIII Secolo." *Antichità Viva* XIII (1974): 61–65.

GIAMPAOLO, *ARTE ILLUSTRATA*, 1974

———. "Per il Malosso disegnatore." *Arte Illustrata* LVII (March 1974): 18–35.

GRASSI, 1968

Grassi, L. *Il libro dei disegni di Jacopo Palma il Giovane all'Accademia di San Luca.* Rome, 1968.

DE GROOT AND SPIES, 1926

de Groot, C. H., and Spies, W. "Die Rheinlandschaften von Lambert Doomer." *Wallraf-Richartz. Jahrbuch* IV (1926): 183–198.

HANNEMA, 1955

Hannema, D. *Catalogue of the H. E. ten Cate Collection.* Rotterdam, 1955.

HARTT, 1958

Hartt, Frederick. *Giulio Romano.* 2 vols. New Haven, 1958.

HASSELT, 1961

Hasselt, Carlos van. *150 tekeningen uit vier eeuwen uit de verzameling van Sir Bruce en Lady Ingram.* Rotterdam, 1961.

HASSELT, 1972

———. *Flemish Drawings of the 17th Century from the Collection of Frits Lugt.* Paris, 1972.

HASSELT, 1974

———. *Dessins Flamands et Hollandais du Dix-Septième Siècle.* Paris: Institut Néerlandais, 1974.

HAVERKAMP-BEGEMANN, 1976

Haverkamp-Begemann, E. "The Youthful Work of Andries Both: His Landscape Drawings." *Print Review* V (Spring 1976): 88–95.

HAVERKAMP-BEGEMANN AND LOGAN, 1969

Haverkamp-Begemann, E., and Logan, A. M. *Rembrandt after Three Hundred Years.* Chicago: Art Institute of Chicago, 1969.

HELD, 1959

Held, Julius S. *Rubens: Selected Drawings.* London, 1959.

HERMITAGE, 1958

Musée de l'Ermitage. Département de l'Art Occidental. Catalogue des Peintures. Leningrad: Hermitage Museum, 1958.

HESELTINE, 1910

Original Drawings by Old Masters of the Dutch School in the Collection of J. P. Heseltine. London, 1910.

HESS, 1935

Hess, Jacob. *Agostino Tassi der Lehrer des Claude Lorrain.* Munich, 1935.

HESS, 1954

————. "Tassi, Bonzi e Cortona a Palazzo Mattei." *Commentari* v (1954): 303–315.

HIND, 1915–1932

Hind, Arthur M. *Catalogue of Drawings of Dutch and Flemish Artists preserved in the Department of Prints and Drawings in the British Museum.* 5 vols. London, 1915–1932.

HIND, 1923

————. *A Catalogue of Rembrandt's Etchings.* 2d ed. 2 vols. London, 1923.

HIND, 1938–1948

————. *Early Italian Engraving.* 7 vols. London, 1938–1948.

HOETINCK, 1961

"Heemskerck en het zestiende eeuwse spiritualisme." *Bulletin of Museum Boymans–van Beuningen* XII (1961): 12–25.

HOLKHAM, 1977

Old Master Drawings from Holkham. London: Thos. Agnew and Sons, Ltd., 1977.

HOLLAND, 1961

Holland, Ralph. *The Carracci: Drawings and Paintings.* Newcastle-upon-Tyne: King's College, 1961.

HOLLSTEIN, 1949–

Hollstein, F. W. H. *Dutch and Flemish Etchings, Engravings and Woodcuts, ca. 1450–1700.* Amsterdam, 1949–.

HOUBRAKEN, 1718

Houbraken, A. *De Groote Schouburgh,* vol. I. Amsterdam, 1718.

HOUTHAKKER, 1965

Master Drawings. Amsterdam: Bernard Houthakker Galleries, 1965.

INSTITUT NÉERLANDAIS, 1974

Acquisitions récentes de toutes époques, Fondation Custodia Collection Frits Lugt. Paris: Institut Néerlandais, 1974.

JUDSON, 1970

Judson, J. Richard. *Dirck Barendsz.* Amsterdam, 1970.

KAMENSKAJA, 1937
Kamenskaja, T. "Unveröffentlichte Zeichnungen Abraham Bloemaerts in der Ermitage." *Oud Holland* LIV (1937): 145–163.

KERRICH, 1829
Kerrich, T. *A Catalogue of the Prints . . . after Martin Heemskerck*. London, 1829.

KITSON, 1973
Kitson, Michael, ed. *Salvator Rosa*. London: Arts Council, 1973.

KRUFT, 1969
Kruft, Hanno-Walter. "Ein Album mit Portraitzeichnungen Ottavio Leonis." *Storia dell'Arte* IV (1969): 447–458.

KUZNETSOV AND TSESJKOWSKAJA, 1972
Kuznetsov, J. and Tsesjkowskaja, T. A. *Hollandse en Vlaamse tekeningen uit de zeventiende eeuw; verzameling van de Hermitage, Leningrad en het Museum Poesjkin, Moskou*. Brussels, 1972.

LANKHEIT, 1959
Lankheit, Klaus. "Il Giornale del Foggini." *Rivista d'Arte* XXXIV (1959): 55–92.

LANKHEIT, 1962
———. *Florentinische Barockplastik*. Munich, 1962.

LANZI, 1796
Lanzi, Abbé Luigi. *History of Painting in Italy*. 1796. Translated by T. Roscoe. London, 1852–1854.

LAVALLÉE, 1930
Lavallée, P. *Le dessin français du XIIIe au XVIe siècle*. Paris: Ecole des Beaux-Arts, 1930.

LEVEY, 1964
Levey, Michael. *The Later Italian Pictures in the Collection of Her Majesty the Queen*. London, 1964.

LONDON, 1932
Exhibition of French Art 1200–1900. London: Royal Academy of Arts, 1932.

LORET, 1935
Loret, Mattia. "Pier Leone Ghezzi." *Capitolium* (1935), pp. 291–307.

LORNA LOWE, 1974
Old Master Drawings Presented by Lorna Lowe. London: Christopher Drake Ltd., 1974.

LOWE, 1976
Lowe, Lorna. *Old Master Drawings*. London: National Book League, 1976.

LUGT, 1920
Lugt, Frits. *Mit Rembrandt in Amsterdam*. Berlin, 1920.

LUGT, 1949
————. *Musée du Louvre, Inventaire Général des Dessins des Ecoles du Nord publié sous les auspices du Cabinet des Dessins. Ecole Flamande*. 2 vols. Paris, 1949.

MAHON, 1968
Mahon, Denis. *Il Guercino: Catalogo Critico dei Dipinti*. Bologna, 1968.

MAHON, 1969
————. *Il Guercino: Catalogo Critico dei Disegni*. Bologna, 1969.

MAHONEY, 1977
Mahoney, Michael. *The Drawings of Salvator Rosa*. New York, 1977.

MANNING, 1968
Manning, Robert L. Introduction to *Drawings of Luca Cambiaso*. New York: Finch College Museum of Art, 1968.

MARIACHER, 1968
Mariacher, G. *Palma il Vecchio*. Milan, 1968.

MARTIN, 1965
Martin, J. R. *The Farnese Gallery*. Princeton, 1965.

MEIJER, 1974
Meijer, Bert. "Early Drawings by Titian: Some Attributions." *Arte Veneta* XXVIII (1974): 75–92.

METROPOLITAN MUSEUM, 1975
Drawings Recently Acquired, 1972–1975. New York: Metropolitan Museum of Art, 1975.

METROPOLITAN MUSEUM, 1976
Roman Artists of the 17th Century, Drawings and Prints. New York: Metropolitan Museum of Art, 1976.

MEYERS, 1975
Meyers, Mary L. *Architectural and Ornament Drawings: Juvarra, Vanvitelli, the Bibiena Family and Other Italian Draughtsmen*. New York: Metropolitan Museum of Art, 1976.

MEZZETTI, 1955
Mezzetti, Amalia. "Contributi a Carlo Maratti." *Rivista dell'Istituto Nazionale d'Archeologia e Storia dell'Arte*, N.S. IV (1955): 253–354.

VAN MOLTKE, 1965
van Moltke, J. W. *Govaert Flinck 1615–1660*. Amsterdam, 1965.

MONACI, 1974

Monaci, Lucia. "Inediti Fogginiani." *Paragone* xxv, no. 289 (March 1974): 48–67.

MONGAN AND SACHS, 1940

Mongan, Agnes, and Sachs, Paul J. *Drawings in the Fogg Museum of Art.* Cambridge, Mass., 1940.

MORGAN, 1824

Morgan, Lady Sydney. *The Life and Times of Salvator Rosa.* London, 1824.

NIELSON, 1969

Nielson, Nancy Ward. "The Quadroni di S. Carlo and Cyclical Imagery of the Time." In *Il Duomo di Milano, Congresso Internazionale.* Milan, 1969.

NIELSON, 1972

————. *Italian Drawings Selected from Midwestern Collections.* St. Louis: St. Louis Art Museum, 1972.

OBERHUBER, "PERINO," 1966

Oberhuber, Konrad. "Observations on Perino del Vaga as a Draughtsman." *Master Drawings* IV (1966): 170–182.

OBERHUBER, *RENAISSANCE,* 1966

————. *Renaissance in Italien 16. Jahrhundert. Die Kunst der Graphik,* vol. 3. Vienna: Graphische Sammlung Albertina, 1966.

OBERHUBER, 1972

————. *Raphaels Zeichnungen.* Berlin, 1972.

OBERHUBER, 1973

Levenson, Jay; Oberhuber, Konrad; and Sheehan, Jacquelyn. *Early Italian Engravings from the National Gallery of Art.* Washington, D.C.: National Gallery of Art, 1973.

OBERHUBER, 1976

————. *Disegni di Tiziano e della sua cerchia.* Venice: Fondazione Giorgio Cini, 1976.

OSTROW, 1968

Ostrow, Stephen. *Visions and Revisions.* Providence: Museum of Art, Rhode Island School of Design, 1968.

OVERSTONE, 1875–1877

Catalogue of Works of Art at Overstone Park, Lockinge House and Carleton Gardens. London, 1875–1877.

PANVINI-ROSATI, 1968

Panvini-Rosati, F. *Medaglie e placchette italiani dal rinascimento al XVIII secolo.* Rome, 1968.

PARISET, 1961

Pariset, F.-G. "Bellange et Lagneau." In *Acts of the Twentieth Congress of the History of Art*, vol. 3. Princeton, 1961.

PARKER, 1929

Parker, K. T. "Lambert Doomer." *Old Master Drawings* IV (1929): 9.

PARKER, 1956

————. *Catalogue of the Collection of Drawings in the Ashmolean Museum*, vol. 2. Oxford, 1956.

PERCY, 1971

Percy, Anne. *Giovanni Benedetto Castiglione: Master Draughtsman of the Italian Baroque*. Philadelphia: Philadelphia Museum of Art, 1971.

PIERSON, 1942

Pierson, W. H. "Drawings of Rubens and Poussin from the Antique." *Marsyas* II (1942): 169–170.

POENSGEN, 1967

Poensgen, Thomas. "Some Unknown Drawings by Domenico Maria Canuti." *Master Drawings* V (1967): 165–168.

POIRIER, 1970

Poirier, M. "The Role of the Concept of *Disegno* in Mid-Sixteenth Century Florence." In *The Age of Vasari*. Notre Dame, Indiana: Art Gallery, University of Notre Dame, 1970.

POOL, ca. 1720–1725

Pool, Matthys. *Verscheide Gedagten in het Koper gebragt, naar de originalen Tekeningen van Rembrandt dor M. Pool. . . .* N.p. (ca. 1720–1725).

POPHAM, 1932

Popham, A. E. *Catalogue of Drawings by Dutch and Flemish Artists Preserved in the Department of Prints and Drawings in the British Museum*. London, 1932.

POPHAM, 1971

————. *Catalogue of the Drawings of Parmigianino*. 3 vols. New Haven, 1971.

POPHAM AND WILDE, 1949

Popham, A. E., and Wilde, J. *The Italian Drawings of the XV and XVI Centuries in the Collection of His Majesty the King at Windsor Castle*. London, 1949.

POSNER, 1971

Posner, Donald. *Annibale Carracci*. London, 1971.

POUNCEY AND GERE, 1962

Pouncey, Philip, and Gere, John A. *Italian Drawings in the British Museum. Raphael and His Circle*. London, 1962.

PRYBRAM-GLADONA, 1969

Prybram-Gladona, C. von. *Unbekannte Handzeichnungen alter Meister aus Europäischem Privatbesitz.* Munich, 1969.

REARICK, 1959

Rearick, W. R. "Battista Franco and the Grimani Chapel." *Saggi e memorie di storia dell'arte* II (1958–1959): 105–139.

RÉAU, 1955–1959

Réau, L. *Iconographie de l'Art Chrétien.* 6 vols. Paris, 1955–1959.

VAN REGTEREN ALTENA AND WARD-JACKSON, 1970

van Regteren Altena, I. Q., and Ward-Jackson, P. W. *Drawings from the Teyler Museum, Haarlem.* London, 1970.

REINHART, 1960

Reinhart, S. "Poussin et la famille del Pozzo." In *Colloque Poussin.* Edited by André Chastel. Paris: Musée du Louvre, 1960.

REINSCH, 1967

Reinsch, Adelheid. *Die Zeichnungen des Marten de Vos.* Ph.D. dissertation, Tübingen, 1964. Bamberg, 1967.

RISD, 1971

Caricature and Its Role in Graphic Satire. Providence: Museum of Art, Rhode Island School of Design, 1971.

ROBINSON, 1869

Robinson, J. C. *Descriptive Catalogue of the Drawings by the Old Masters Forming the Collection of John Malcolm of Poltalloch, Esq.* London, 1869.

ROBINSON, 1958–1974

Robinson, M. S. *Van de Velde Drawings; a Catalogue of Drawings in the National Maritime Museum Made by the Elder and the Younger Willem van de Velde.* 2 vols. Cambridge, England, 1958–1974.

ROBINSON, 1977

Robinson, Franklin. *Seventeenth Century Dutch Drawings from American Collections.* Washington, D.C.: International Exhibitions Foundation, 1977.

ROETTGEN, 1973

Roettgen, Herward R. *Il Cavaliere d'Arpino.* Rome: Palazzo Venezia, 1973.

ROLI, 1969

Roli, R. *I disegni italiani del seicento.* Treviso, 1969.

ROSAND AND MURARO, 1976–1977

Rosand, David, and Muraro, Michelangelo. *Titian and the Venetian Woodcut.* Washington, D.C.: International Exhibitions Foundation, 1976–1977.

ROWLANDS, 1964
Rowlands, John. "Mola's Preparatory Drawings and Some Additions to his Oeuvre." *Master Drawings* II (1964): 271–276.

ROYAL ACADEMY, 1938
Catalogue of the Exhibition of 17th-Century Art in Europe, 1938. London: Royal Academy of Arts, 1938.

ROYAL ACADEMY, 1953
Drawings by Old Masters. London: Royal Academy of Arts, 1953.

RUDOLF, 1962
Old Master Drawings from the Collection of Mr. C. R. Rudolf. London: Arts Council, 1962.

SALERNO, 1963
Salerno, Luigi. *Salvator Rosa.* Milano, 1963.

SALERNO, 1970
———. "Il dissenso nella pittura; intorno a Filippo Napoletano, Caroselli, Salvator Rosa e altri." *Storia dell'Arte* V (1970): 32–65.

SAXL, 1939–1940
Saxl, F. "The Battle Scene Without a Hero: Aniello Falcone and his Patrons." *Journal of the Warburg and Courtauld Institutes* III (1939–1940): 70–87.

SCHAB, 1970
A Collection of Fifty Master Drawings from the 15th to the 20th Century. New York: William H. Schab Gallery, 1970.

SCHATBORN, 1974
Schatborn, Peter. "Een Toegeschriving an Govaert Flinck." *Bulletin van het Rijksmuseum,* no. 22 (1974), pp. 113–121; English summary pp. 126–127.

SCHMIDT, 1932
Schmidt, H. W. "Drawings by Salvator Rosa in the Leipzig Stadtbibliothek." *Old Master Drawings* VI (1932): 60–61.

SCHULZ, DOOMER, 1974
Schulz, W. *Lambert Doomer Sämtliche Zeichnungen.* Berlin, 1974.

SCHULZ, LANDSCHAFTSZEICHNUNG, 1974
———. *Die Holländische Landschaftszeichnung 1600–1740.* Berlin: Staatliche Museen Preussischer Kulturbesitz, 1974.

SELIGMAN AND CO., 1925
Original Drawings by the Old Masters. New York: Seligman and Co., 1925.

SLIVE, 1964
Slive, Seymour. "Reconsideration of Some Rejected Rembrandt Drawings." *Art Quarterly* XXVII (1964): 276–295.

SLIVE, 1975
———. "Rembrandt's Man Wearing a Plumed Beret and Gorget, a Recent Acquisition." *Bulletin of the Detroit Institute of Arts* LIV (1975): 1–14.

SMDSKAYA, 1962
Smdskaya, N. *Teniers*. Editions du Musée de L'Ermitage, Leningrad, 1962.

SMYTH, 1971
Smyth, Craig Hugh. *Bronzino as Draughtsman, an Introduction*. Locust Valley, New York, 1971.

STAMPFLE, 1969
Stampfle, Felice, et al. *Rembrandt: Experimental Etcher*. Boston: Museum of Fine Arts, 1969.

STAMPFLE AND BEAN, 1967
Stampfle, Felice, and Bean, Jacob. *The Seventeenth Century in Italy. Drawings from New York Collections*, vol. 2. New York: Metropolitan Museum of Art, 1967.

STECHOW, 1929
Stechow, Wolfgang. "Peeter van Hoeck (active in the early seventeenth century)." *Old Master Drawings* IV (December 1929): 45.

STECHOW, 1975
———. "Verhaecht and Houck, Teacher and Pupil." *Master Drawings* XIII (Summer 1975): 145–147.

STIX, 1932
Stix, Alfred, and Fröhlich-Bum, L. *Beschreibender Katalog der Handzeichnungen in der Graphischen Sammlung Albertina, Die Zeichnungen der Toskanischen, Umbrischen und Römischen Schulen*. Vienna, 1932.

STOCKHOLM, 1953
Dutch and Flemish Drawings. Stockholm: National Museum, 1953.

STUBBE, 1966
Stubbe, Wolf. *Zeichnungen Alter Meister aus Deutschem Privatbesitz*. Bremen, 1966.

STUFFMANN, 1968
Stuffmann, M. "Les Tableaux de la Collection de Pierre Crozat." *Gazette des Beaux-Arts* LXXII (July 1968): 11–142.

SUIDA MANNING AND SUIDA, 1958
Suida Manning, Bertina, and Suida, Wilhelm. *Luca Cambiaso: La Vita e le Opere*. Milan, 1958.

SUMOWSKI, 1965
Sumowski, Werner. "Notizen zu Zeichnungen von F. Bol." In *Festschrift für Edouard Trautscholdt*. Hamburg, 1965.

SUMOWSKI, 1975

———. "Zeichnungen von Lastman und aus dem Lastman-Kreis." *Giessener Beiträge zur Kunstgeschichte* III (1975): 174.

SUTHERLAND HARRIS, 1964

Sutherland Harris, Ann. "Pier Francesco Mola—His Visits to North Italy and His Residence in Rome." *The Burlington Magazine* CVI (1964): 363–368.

SUTHERLAND HARRIS AND SCHAAR, 1967

Sutherland Harris, Ann, and Schaar, Eckhard. *Die Handzeichnungen von Andrea Sacchi und Carlo Maratta. Kataloge des Kunstmuseums Düsseldorf, Handzeichnungen.* Vol. 1. Düsseldorf, 1967.

YVONNE TAN-BUNZL, 1975

Old Master Drawings and French Drawings of the Nineteenth Century. London: Yvonne Tan-Bunzl, 1975.

THOMAS, 1916

Thomas, T. H. "Ottavio Leoni—a Forgotten Portraitist." *Print Collector's Quarterly* VI (December 1916): 323–375.

TIETZE AND TIETZE-CONRAT, 1944

Tietze, Hans, and Tietze-Conrat, Erica. *The Drawings of the Venetian Painters in the 15th and 16th Centuries.* New York, 1944.

TOISON D'OR, 1904

Liste Nominale des Chevaliers de l'Ordre Illustre de la Toison d'Or. N.p., 1904.

TÜMPEL, 1974

Tümpel, Astrid. *The Pre-Rembrandtists.* Sacramento: E. B. Crocker Art Gallery, 1974.

VALENTINER, 1925–1934

Valentiner, W. R. *Rembrandt. Des Meisters Handzeichnungen.* 2 vols. Stuttgart, 1925–1934.

VALENTINER, 1967

———. "Notes on Old and Modern Drawings: Drawings by Bol." *Art Quarterly* XX (Spring 1967): 49–70.

VASARI-GRONAU, 1904–1927

Vasari, Giorgio. *Die Lebensbeschreibungen der berühmtesten Architekten, Bildhauer und Maler.* Edited by A. Gottschewski and G. Gronau. Strasburg, 1904–1927.

VASARI-MILANESI, 1878–1885

———. *Le Opere di Giorgio Vasari con Nuove Annotazioni e Commenti di Gaetano Milanesi.* 7 vols. Florence, 1878–1885.

VENTURI, 1925

Venturi, A. *Storia dell'Arte Italiana*, vol. 9. Milan, 1925.

VEY, 1958

A Catalogue of Drawings by European Masters in the Worcester Art Museum. Worcester, Mass., 1958.

VIATTE, 1974

Viatte, Françoise. *Dessins de Stefano della Bella 1610–1664.* Musée du Louvre. Cabinet des Dessins. Inventaire général des dessins italiens, vol. 2. Paris, 1974.

VLIEGHE, 1961–1966

Vlieghe, H. "David II Teniers (1610–1690) en het Hof van Aartshertog Leopold-Wilhelm en Don Juan van Oostenrijk—1647–1659." *Gentse Bijdragen tot de Kunstgeschiedenis en de Oudheidkunde* XIX (1961–1966): 123–149.

WADDINGHAM, 1964

Waddingham, M. R. "Andries and Jan Both in France and Italy." *Paragone* XV, no. 171 (March 1964): 13–43.

WATERHOUSE, 1967

Waterhouse, Ellis. "An Immaculate Conception by G. B. Castiglione." *The Minneapolis Institute of Arts Bulletin* LVI (1967): 5–10.

WEIGEL, 1865

Weigel, Rudolf. *Die Werke der Maler in Ihren Handzeichnungen.* Leipzig, 1865.

WHITE, 1974

White, Christopher. "Dutch Landscapes from the Collection of Harry G. Sperling." *Master Drawings* XII (1974): 40–41.

WIND, 1944

Wind, Edgar. "Sante Pagnini and Michelangelo: A Study of the Succession of Savonarola." *Gazette des Beaux-Arts* XXVI (July 1944): 211–246.

WITTKOWER, 1952

Wittkower, Rudolf. *The Drawings of the Carracci in the Collection of Her Majesty the Queen at Windsor Castle.* London, 1952.

WOODNER, 1971

Woodner Collection I: A Selection of Old Master Drawings before 1700. New York: William H. Schab Galleries, 1971.

WURZBACH, 1906–1911

Wurzbach, A. von. *Niederländisches Künstler-Lexikon.* 3 vols. Vienna and Leipzig, 1906–1911.